"Is 'Peckerhead' Hyphenated?"
Building the International Space Station

Vincent de Cordoba

1999

Copyright © 1999 by Vincent de Cordoba

ISBN 0-7414-0125-8

Published by:

PUBLISHING.COM

Infinity Publishing.com
519 West Lancaster Avenue
Haverford, PA 19041-1413
Info@buybooksontheweb.com
www.buybooksontheweb.com
Toll-free (877) BUY BOOK
Local Phone (610) 520-2500
Fax (610) 519-0261

Printed in the United States of America

Printed on Recycled Paper

Published January-2001

To The Captain and to SZR
for their guidance and wisdom.

And for my Uncle William -
with whom, it now seems,
I have one more thing in common.

Preface

This is my personal story about the building of the International Space Station. It was constructed around actual quotes from real people; quotes I recorded and collected during the nine years that I worked on the International Space Station project.

As the years passed, I wrote down hundreds of these witty and piercing remarks as they so accurately and elegantly described our 'character-building' situation. I accumulated them on all sorts of different scraps of paper, including paper napkins and boarding-pass stubs. My friends at work would occasionally stop by my office and we'd rummage through the heap and pull out one quote after another, laughing anew and reiterating the important characteristics of each - who, when, where - like wine connoisseurs. "You should write a book", they'd often say. Some time around my seventh or eighth year with the project, I sorted through all those quotes and began writing. The quotes are perfectly intact, captured exactly as I first heard them. This book, these quotes, tell a true story.

For insurance reasons, however, I make no claim that this book is an authoritative text on the International Space Station or any other subject. It is simply one man's record of a large-scale engineering adventure, offering the reader a unique insight into the human side of building such a space vehicle. Furthermore, in the spirit of generosity, fictitious names in this story bravely substitute for the real characters and most of the real organizations that actually lived it.

While this book is likely to give the reader a startling glimpse into a frustrating world of unchecked bureaucracy and to-be-expected human rivalry, it is important to acknowledge the magnificent achievement of the *individuals* who overcame all the obstacles and eventually succeeded in achieving such an ambitious goal. Technically, managerially, politically, financially and multiculturally, the International Space Station was a tremendous project to undertake.

The people who made it happen were dedicated adventurers who never gave up. They endured recurring threats of cancellation by Congress, often-shaky relations among the international partners, incessant redesigns, perennial budget cutbacks, fire-drill schedules, trendy management reorganizations, costly family sacrifices, and certainly no shortage of SOB's. They were true to themselves and their conviction to succeed. They weathered all the damage merchants who existed only to hurt the collective goal, as well as the impressive number of zeros who did nothing but soak up the money. And, in the end, their tenacity prevailed. They did it. They realized the dream. Bravo!

This story was not written for the mass market (or any other market, for that matter). I wrote it in the hope that someone curious might read it a hundred years from now, or even a thousand, and maybe connect and *feel* just what it was like to be there with us, building the International Space Station.

Contents

When I first joined Resistoglide, a few weeks after funding for the Space Station project was authorized, I proudly and enthusiastically signed on to build a manned space vehicle which would orbit the earth for fifteen years or more, serving as a laboratory for earth observation and scientific experiments in zero gravity with aspirations for evolving into a base from which to launch a manned mission to Mars. Quite the dream job for any young engineer, especially *this* Star Trek fan (the original series, just for the record).

Entrusted to the National Aeronautics and Space Administration (NASA), with its long history of success in space exploration, the Space Station was to be a large-scale functional habitat that had to operate in the harsh environment of space with minimum risk to its crew, itself, and its payloads. It had to withstand stressful pressure differentials created by the vacuum of space, extremely cold temperatures, and continual exposure to corrosive space particles. It was to orbit the earth every 90 minutes; 60 minutes exposed to sunlight and 30 minutes in the dark. It required a power system (which had to provide power during the dark period of the orbit as well as in sunlight), a guidance and navigation system, a communications system, thermal control systems, a life support system, and myriad other computer-controlled capabilities. A triple-redundant set of command and control computers would coordinate the overall operation of the vehicle and all its systems and subsystems.

Every one of the vehicle's systems had to meet its functional, performance and resource-allocation requirements (i.e., it had to do X, Y and Z, *this* accurately and *that* fast, within specified power, weight, and computer resource limits). All the systems were to be built by *different* teams of engineers, working for *different* contractors and subcontractors, in *different* states and countries, and had to work together perfectly. The hardware and software components within each system and subsystem had to be integrated together and fine-tuned for optimal performance. Sophisticated engineering models and prototypes had to be built to test all the pieces before putting them together. *Millions* of pieces of engineering data needed to be derived, tracked and kept up to date without error.

Adding to the technical challenge, the Space Station was to be constructed in stages. Large, pressurized modules, in which the crew could breathe and move around, were planned for its center. These pressurized modules connected to external truss elements that extended out to massive solar array modules on the port and starboard wings. Due to the Space Station's not-so-curious interdependency on the Space Shuttle (which has a relatively small cargo carrying capability), over forty flights would be required to complete the assembly sequence.

Not an easy project to pull off.

3.1.2.2 The Engineering Business

Aerospace engineering, and perhaps engineering in general, seems to be characterized by a few distinctive peculiarities which include less-than-exemplary oral and written communication skills, modest salary ceilings, and a phase-delayed dress code (stuck in the 1950's, 60's, 70's or 80's).

"Everyone knows engineers can't write!" is a phrase I first heard in college. I heard it again many times over as a professional engineer working on the Space Station. It wasn't stated so much as an apologetic acknowledgement accompanied by an earnest desire to learn how to write but more so as a liberating declaration that granted all engineers a waiver from having to write properly (or even adequately). And this special entitlement to exercise poor grammar was not exclusive to the written form of communication. There were, however, on occasion, short-lived flashes of accuracy, as showcased during a telephone conference call (or 'telecon', as they were known) with Earl Marlborough of NASA:

Jose Cabesagrande: "Then [given that particular scenario], you can't orientate the radiators?"

Vincent de Cordoba: "*Orientate* ?!?! Don't you mean *pointentate*?"

Earl Marlborough: "Hey, Jose made a *logicated* guess!"

I first joined Resistoglide, the prime contractor responsible for the Space Station Electric Power System (EPS), as a system design engineer in January of 1988. Two and a half years later, I was appointed to lead the

EPS Control System Design team after the previous manager of that team (then my boss, Carl Stevenson) let his inbox overflow onto the floor and out the door to the point where his superiors got the message that he couldn't take the management headaches any more and wanted out. I came to the same conclusion every day for the next five years but used a more subtle, albeit somewhat slower-acting, strategy to make my exit.

Jose Cabesagrande was the first person I recruited in building up the crew at the heart of my team. His lack of polish was not a factor in that decision (Jose was extremely proud that his intimate knowledge of every single fast-food restaurant in the San Fernando Valley afforded him a unique navigational coordinate system). In spite of his eating habits, Jose was made of the right material. The picture of John Gotti on the door of the office that we shared (before they gave me my own 'manager's office') kept everybody guessing, and Jose and I enjoyed a famously effective partnership for years.

Earl Marlborough was our NASA customer (the NASA point of contact for our area of responsibility). He worked for NASA Lewis Research Center in Cleveland, Ohio. Earl was the best customer I ever dealt with during my nine-year tenure on the Space Station project. He had a rare balance of intelligence, dedication, personality and sense of humor - just what I'd expect from a fellow Cornellian. We shared an in-depth, first-hand knowledge of miserably cold and wet weather, as well as healthy respect for the benefits and risks of volume-driven beer consumption.

Like a lot of engineers, Earl, Jose, and I went into engineering because we understood and enjoyed math and science and we wanted to build things. A few years after getting into the engineering business, perhaps because of the money, a lot of engineers want to get out. They talk about buying doughnut shop franchises, going to law school, playing the stock market, even getting into ostrich farming. A friend of mine, who also happens to be a Cornellian, Cyrus Koobideh, concisely summed up the general dilemma that frustrates thousands of engineers stuck with mortgage payments, college tuition bills, etc.

"I should really retire by now. Unfortunately, I depend heavily on my income from [the company]."

Cyrus often wondered if he should have pursued an MBA instead of his Ph.D. in Electrical Engineering. It's what you do with what you've got, I say.

One person who was never distracted by money and thoroughly enjoyed being an engineer was Marcus Electricus. Marcus Electricus came to the Space Station project having made his bones in the electrical utilities industry back in Pittsburgh. He really knew his business. He was also a genius (complete with brilliant half and impossible-to-work-with half). What inevitably eroded his working relationship with most of his colleagues was that he was impossible to depend on, he stuck to his sometimes erratic vision, he was convinced he was right, and he didn't hold back his contempt for rules, procedures, forms, bureaucrats, meetings and incompetents. Unhappy that Resistoglide's management was not going to provide him with the resources he needed to develop his brilliant simulation of the EPS, Marcus took a job with Stylish Glass Towers (SGT), one of the other prime contractors on the project. The remarkable thing was that he didn't quit Resistoglide. He just added a second full-time job to his first full-time job. His allegiance was always to his mission:

12

"Just like electrons, I recognize no Work Package [contractor/contractual] boundaries."

After nearly a year of driving over 180 miles a day and making do without some of the basic necessities in life (like sleep and seeing one's family), Marcus Electricus said goodbye to SGT and came back, exclusively, to Resistoglide. He had built the lab at SGT, and Resistoglide had, as he put it, come around to his way of thinking.

Marcus Electricus was extremely well read and a great social companion with whom to exchange philosophical ideas and discuss almost any subject. Ever insightful, and amiably blunt, he was never afraid to make the situation perfectly clear:

Marcus Electricus: "Well, Vincent, anything you want to know?"

Vincent de Cordoba: "I want to know how to get a Ferrari by next week."

Marcus Electricus: "I think you made a mistake about twenty years ago."

The 'mistake', of course, was going into engineering. I haven't given up on my goal to get the Ferrari without having to renounce engineering. At least I can afford to wear Italian shoes (which, Italian engineers being the exception, is far from the hideous norm in the engineering business).

Stereotypically speaking, the clothes engineers wear seem to have provided more than an average amount of entertainment for a large segment of the general public over the years. Many of the stories about short-sleeved, pocket-protected shirts, stained brown polyester ties, poly-blend pants, and thick-rubber-sponge-soled shoes were decisively substantiated on a regular basis by actual characters on the Space Station project. Those guys either didn't know or didn't care. But that was not the funny part. What really left one wondering about the greater order of the universe was the fact that everyday (before the trendy conversion down to casual wear and then back up a bit to 'business casual') my colleagues dressed up in spiffy business attire (not exactly Wall Street or Saville Row, but jacket and tie nonetheless) to work in a forty-year-old, windowless, hangar-like facility, with visible-steel-girder ceiling motif (encrusted with coral-like asbestos formations) - all painted in traditional tones of possibly-hip-in-the-fifties yellowy beige and industrial gray.

Now is a good time to introduce Archie D'Arc. Archie D'Arc was a long-time member of my crew who came out to California from Boston (Medfield, to be exact). He had just graduated from a very famous engineering school. The first time I met him, he was interviewing for a job at Resistoglide, and he was presenting to our management some of the work he had just completed to earn his Master's degree. I asked him if he'd ever been bowling at 'The Hong Kong', and we connected immediately.

Unfortunately for Archie, he got the job. It didn't take him long to decide that he wanted to get off the technical path and get into management. That was step one. Step two is still in the works so I cannot say more about that at this time. For a 'fucking technologist' (as he was once called after slamming an opponent into the boards while playing hockey for his school), he had a marvelously quick wit (which tilted toward the parched side of dry) and a mischievous sense of humor. One day, he dared the system by showing up at work without a tie. This was highly irregular. We all wore ties. The Resistoglide dress code said we had to. That was aerospace industry standard. When asked about his deviation from the long-established dress code regulations, he told us:

"I realized, who are we trying to kid when we sit in a warehouse and wear a tie?!"

Archie D'Arc had looked at the emperor, and his eminence was naked. It just takes a while for a profession like engineering (which is simultaneously encouraged and held back by tradition) to accept such a drastic change to the long-established order of things.

3.1.2.3 *Esteemed Colleagues*

The Space Station project began with the official authorization for funding from the United States government in late 1987. I was given a job offer contingent upon that authorization, and I began work with Resistoglide on the first working day in January (this was when I learned that companies don't like to hire people before the Christmas holidays so they don't have to pay for their vacations). With Christmas out of the way, there was a rush to hire all the people needed to do the job. Every week, new people joined the organization and filled the job slots described in the proposals. Screening for the best candidates took a back seat to staffing the organization as quickly as possible, which, not to withhold acknowledgement where acknowledgement is due, led to some of the choice material in this book.

The mix of staff included:

- 'old guys' from previous aerospace programs like the Space Shuttle, Skylab, and Apollo
- government-agent-standards-and-procedures-auditor types who had never been overly challenged by their workload over the years
- new graduates fresh out of engineering school
- ex-military (mostly desk-job) managers
- 'documentation engineers' (it's true)
- 'lab rats' (hands-on, in the lab, anti-authority, ignore the documentation)
- Ph.D. analysts with their big-screen computer monitors and inherent need for publishing innocuous

papers (that all say things like "...encouraging preliminary indications ...further research required...possibility of actual results in the future...") and going to conferences in the usual desirable locations

- long-haired heavy metal fans
- and profanity-free believers in a wide variety of religions

Not to mention all the different ethnicities drawn to, and redefining, Los Angeles.

This mix can lead to some bonus entertainment. One day, Alex, a born-again Christian from Buffalo, was ardently repeating to Ben, an Israeli Jew (knowledgeable and not bashful when it came to religion or politics), his belief that Ben was not going to heaven unless he "accept the Lord Jesus Christ" as his savior. After Ben gave up trying to reason with Alex on an intellectual level, they went and got the text to the Old Testament and continued the argument over the words. The argument finally ended with Ben telling Alex that Alex (still firmly entrenched with his position) didn't know what he was talking about because the translation of the Old Testament text - from Hebrew to English - was...incorrect.

When people work together over a long period of time, their fundamental characteristics are gradually (and sometimes explosively) revealed. Their strengths and weaknesses become apparent to everyone around them. Most people converge upon 'average', putting in the required (standard) hours and doing something mediocre, which is neither worthy of note nor offensive or harmful to others. A select few make an extra effort, do an outstanding job, help others and radiate a genuine positive attitude ('genuine' as opposed to fake, which is, tellingly, and usually rather lamely, put on in the presence of superiors, rarely fooling anyone, including the superiors if they are worth anything). Unavoidably, there are always some people who, instead of working, spend their time deriding others, fertilizing problems and spreading their own bad attitude. Everyone knows who works hard, who is smart, who's faking it, who's lazy, who's hopeless, who is deathlessly negative, who's commitment leaves with the van pool, etc. Which brings us to a revealing collection of criticisms about some colorful individuals who were part of the International Space Station project while I was there -

On the subject of questionable worth:

Vincent de Cordoba: "What's Vespa doing? Is he doing anything?"

Earl Marlborough: "Yeah, he's preventing the chair from floating up to the ceiling by sitting on it in case we lose gravity."

Vespa was a good guy. He just wasn't over exerting himself of late.

Max Schwantz was young, bright and dedicated, and he produced good work. The department he came from had a reputation for world-class paperwork proliferation (mostly over-documenting everything and occasionally talking about other people's work at a harmlessly superficial level). I recruited Max Schwantz to join my crew a few years into the project. He had a natural ability for being a smart alec and regularly had everyone else in stitches (except the poor victim, that is) with his animated stories and clever remarks.

On extending every possible invitation for redemption:

"If he had finagled us and knew what he was doing, I could appreciate that."

-Max Schwantz

On reassuring ourselves in the face of a feeble challenge:

Vincent de Cordoba: "He's got a 'tude [short for attitude]."

Jose Cabesagrande: "Yeah, but we do too. And ours is superior."

On the morale-draining realization that the bureaucracy of our system has proven to be larger than life by its uncanny ability to obstruct the natural selection process:

"He's just one of those guys - life hasn't found a place for him, but Resistoglide provided a home for him."

-Thin Angus

Thin Angus was a black-T-shirt-rock-and-roll-anti-establishment bitter complainer who eventually found another job. Occasionally, though, what he said hit home.

On letting a colleague finish his point and ensuring that he doesn't make another for a while:

"So what Woody is saying is interesting but useless."

-Archie D'Arc

Woody Nelson, although certainly one of the first people I would hire out of all the people I worked with on the project based on his technical knowledge and engineering ability, liked to talk a lot. Admirably, he recognized this trait and often laughed at himself when others teased him (sometimes even holding up a meeting to underline, slowly, that very point).

On providing feedback that the analogy attempted by Woody Nelson confused everyone further:

"No, wait a minute! I got another analogy, Boss! You're holding a pineapple...in an electrical storm..."

-Max Schwantz

On trying to be kind to a non-contributing work colleague by speaking in numerical terms to recognize that at least he doesn't cause problems:

"I wouldn't say he's a positive...but he's at least a zero."

-Archie D'Arc

On a colleague's unusual pastime of carving styrofoam coffee cups during meetings in order to (a) concentrate on the discussion and (b) not fall asleep from the same discussion:

Felix Depeche: "Carving [Bear] designs these un-fucking-biodegradable incredible art forms [made from styrofoam cups]. A hundred years from now, they'll be in some museum while we'll be in the ground."

Bud Hellcat: "Kill him off now to increase their value."

Carving Bear worked for Popular Largeness (another of the prime contractors) in Huntsville, Alabama. He was proud of being part Choctaw Indian. As the reader will discover later on, he had a natural gift for cheerful sarcasm. He was perhaps best known for carving wonderful sculptures out of plain old styrofoam coffee cups during meetings. He said it helped him concentrate. Carving produced many artistic sculptures including castles, knights and dragons, Viking ships, city skylines, roller coasters, animals, and natural landscapes. He often gave these original works of art away. I used to have three, but one was stolen from my office. Of the remaining two, which are now safe at home, my favorite is the aquatic piece with fish and plants below the water and a fishing boat on the surface (complete with fisherman, fishing rod, line and fish on the end of the line) - amazing.

Felix Depeche was a NASA engineer in his early thirties, based in Reston, Virginia. He was post-maturely (I may be inventing this word, but it should work fine) into new wave music. So much so that he regularly went to concerts without his wife and kids (his wife no longer enjoyed large crowds of image-conscious teens while his kids were still a couple of years younger than the kids who went to the shows). He always seemed excited about the latest show he'd seen, but I gradually drifted further and further away from being able to look even the least bit interested. As the years went by, all the latest bands seemed sillier and sillier to me.

Bud Hellcat was also a NASA engineer and also in his early thirties. Hellcat (everyone called him by his last name, even his mother) was a wild-man, action adventure hero from Texas who looked very much like John F. Kennedy. He also possessed a charismatic personality that often livened up what would otherwise have been

21

many a long and dreary project meeting. Hellcat drove a pickup truck that was never-washed and always full of empty beer cans. To my surprise the first time I found out, he read a lot of books and traveled internationally. Most people didn't know that. The unlikely mix of social skills, modern-day-cowboy lifestyle and underlying cultural sophistication always made him great company - a gentleman partyer. His viewpoint reflected that balance:

"I've been thrown in jail three times. Once was a mistake."

-Bud Hellcat

On extending one's reputation:

Sam Ewing: "Was he [Julius Dusenberg] shooting from the hip?"

Vincent de Cordoba: "He was shooting from somewhere in between both hips."

Sam Ewing worked for the most well-known company in the computer business, Serious Contraptions (SC), which had a major role in the station's computer systems. He was one of the senior people working on the Space Station program that I respected most. He had presence. He *was* SC. When Sam Ewing spoke, SC was stating its position. He had built his knowledge and reputation in man-rated space systems (systems that had to support and protect human life in space) and software development on the earlier Space Shuttle program. He had also been married and divorced three times and was dating a twenty-seven-year-old waitress when I last saw him. Sam was cool. Sam had worked with Julius Dusenberg.

Julius Dusenberg was the program manager and president of the organization that built the Space Shuttle. He was razor sharp and possessed a rare combination of vision, conviction, ethics, heart and raw natural ability found in great leaders whose people would follow them anywhere. Julius was brought into the Space Station program as a consultant to overcome the chaos. The first time I met Julius, I had to present our control system design for the Space Station EPS to him at Resistoglide as part of his around-the-country initial investigation into the overall vehicle design. The first thing he did when he entered the room was greet and poke fun at one of our senior directors (who usually commanded a fair degree of respect - or, at least, fear - from the rest of us). Julius asked this director when he was going to get around to taking care of the holes he had left in a Space Shuttle requirements document he was responsible for over a decade ago.

On one of the negative aspects of large (huge), projects and the impersonal nature of big companies:

Vincent de Cordoba: "Fernando, regarding the meeting with the PV [photovoltaic] department - when is good for you?"

Fernando Antofagasta: "I don't even know those assholes."

Fernando Antofagasta was Chilean. He dressed well and kept a low profile. He didn't interact with a lot of people, and most people didn't know who he was. One time, during a department meeting, his boss's boss thought he was a new guy and asked him to introduce himself to the rest of the department - after he'd been with the project for over a year. Fernando eventually left...for another big company.

There are two kinds of people -:

"There are two types of people: meandering generalities and meaningful specifics. He's too much of a meandering generality to pull this off."

-Woody Nelson

On basic character flaws:

"If Bathroom-Locke didn't have such an attitude problem and got a charisma transplant, he could go places."

-Jose Cabesagrande

Ralph Bathroom-Locke was one of those people who thrives on irritating others. The more irate others became because of him, the genuinely happier he was. He used to deride our control system design in public (even in front of the customer - that was his favorite venue) - any chance he could. He would preach about how terrible it was, how it didn't meet the requirements, how we weren't allowed to do this and that, how we should change X to Y, how we needed to put in all this extra functionality, etc., etc.

Tigers fight back. After a few decisive, and humiliating, losses in public battles against a foe he never counted on (us), he withdrew to the background and eventually left the department and then the company, basically neutered. Over the next few years, I learned that the forces of mischief had periodically tried to rehire him, but there were enough people still there to remember the image he built himself, and nobody signed the paperwork.

On prize-winning melons:

Vincent de Cordoba: "Last week we were at 15.5 heads [people] for an 11-head budget."

Archie D'Arc: "That's because Jose's got a really big head."

On tag-team slamming the audacity of claiming great achievement (specifically, claiming to one's superiors to have written a large computer program) in order to disguise an insufferably-limited ability for doing so (or anything else worthwhile):

Marcus Electricus: "He was responsible for about 36 lines of code."

Archie D'Arc: "And one of them was 'End'."

On being very careful to build one's organization with only the best people:

"He's a good guy, but I don't think he's got the right clock speed for our group."

Vincent de Cordoba

On passionately beating the already-very-dead, yes-man horse one more time whenever it was both safe and politically beneficial to do so:

"He's the eighth exclamation point."

Vincent de Cordoba

Certain people infallibly jump to always agree with the customer or the boss, no matter what is said or contradicted, or how many others have just repeated it. It's mystifying to me how long they manage to last.

On accusing someone really deserving, in public, without subtlety:

"It's Yo-Yo's like you who are killing this program!!!"

Earl Marlborough to Herr Objectclassen

These words gushed out of Earl Marlborough towards the end of the 'Freedom' phase of the Space Station project (when it was called 'Space Station *Freedom*'). Herr Objectclassen was a technical guru type who worked for SC. He was responsible for developing the run-time, object-oriented, input/output database design for the end-to-end Space Station's on-orbit avionics (control) system. Tough enough to say. Tougher to build. Earl could see the writing on the wall. As it happened, the Space Station program did not die, but a major reorganization did occur, and when the music stopped, both Earl and Herr Objectclassen wound up without a chair.

On less-than-honorable superiors:

Jose Cabesagrande: "What's his position?"

Larry Tosca: "I think he's a NASA Congressional [*this part is too rude to repeat*]."

Enter Larry Tosca. When the overall management responsibility of the Space Station project was handed to Popular Largeness in 1993, we first met the irreverent, eccentric, Larry Tosca, who came from Seattle. He began working for Popular Largeness the same year I was born. He had attained the elite position of Super Senior Fellow (or some such equivalent), and was basically set for life. His new job title was Space Station Software Architect (*singular* - the architect), and he was responsible for the significant redesign of the troubled end-to-end computer control system that ran all the vehicle's on-board and ground-support systems.

Larry loved opera (he had a collection of over 2000 opera CDs) and drove a Triumph TR6. He was never afraid to speak his mind. In this case, his target was an abrasive and unscrupulous egotist we'll just call El Pricko. This guy really knew how to alienate a room. He got his jollies that way (probably the only way he got them). He angrily spewed his bad manners and protruded into the space of all those around him except, of course, his boss (whom he sucked up to very nicely). Larry figured him out and wasn't intimidated.

A big bag of dried fruit and mixed nuts comes to mind when I think about some of the characters I encountered on the Space Station project. Fertile ground for psychological harvesting. It wasn't easy getting things done given such a mutual lack of respect for one another.

3.1.2.4 Social Constant

Socializing is a common part of any job or project where people work together, especially for an extended (and, boy, was it extended) period of time. Non-work-related subject matter is a refreshing detour from the business. Everyone learns who likes what, and friendships are built. I befriended a lot of people while working on the Space Station.

Brother Erasmo was, I suppose, my best friend from the Space Station project (no doubt this declaration will inflate his inflated head further). We happened to be members of the same college fraternity though we had attended different schools. We were also only within a few months of each other in age, and we shared similar values such as making fun of the deserving, including each other. It wasn't enough to simply poke fun at something or someone; it had to be done with confidence and a touch of flair:

"I'll tell you how I'm going to win this argument, and I'm going to stoop to your level to do it."

-Brother Erasmo

There was a period in time when Erasmo and I used to go out on the town every weekend in the company of our trusty friend, J.D., spend a lot of money, and wind up at our favorite diner on Santa Monica Boulevard (which featured our always personable, ever tolerant, certified-public-accountant, good-friend waiter from Egypt). Eating breakfast at two in the morning after drinking for five or six hours had a wonderfully restorative effect. So we always tried to save a few dollars for food.

In 1993, Erasmo and I went to Palm Springs for Memorial Day weekend, to relive the memorable time we had there the year before. Poolside parties, silicon-enhanced bikini contest, the power of a fake cell phone *(Arzo!!!)*, lots of beer and too much sun. After the first day of the festivities that continued well into the night, far from the diner on Santa Monica Boulevard, I awoke the next morning to Erasmo's humble murmuring as he stared at a single, mangy looking dollar that lay wet and crumpled inside his wallet:

"I think I need to eat...which means I need to find a Bank of America."

Back at the work place, lunch time was a necessary departure from the constant commotion of the job. Although we sometimes worked well into the lunch hour (occasionally missing it altogether), we usually managed to get away, do the eating and take care of some business. We planned most of our battle strategies at lunch. Lunch was important to us, and, whenever possible, we left a few minutes early. We weren't afraid to be challenged by any of the company 'policemen' because we were ready to lash back with a retort that would compare the hundreds of uncompensated hours any one of us put in every year to his clock-watching, 40-hour-try-to-look-busy week, escape-via-van-pool work regimen and invert their fundamental argument.

Vincent de Cordoba: "Yo, Jose!"

Jose Cabesagrande: "Speak!"

Vincent de Cordoba: "Do you know what time it is?"

Jose Cabesagrande: "It's lunch time!"

Vincent de Cordoba: "It's past lunch time - it's almost 12:00!"

Probably the most colorful social operator I, or anyone else, ever encountered while working on the Space Station was a guy named Arzo. Arzo was a supreme master of the art of socializing. He knew <u>everybody</u>. He could charm his way into any club, bar, restaurant, or show for free most of the time. He knew all the bouncers and all the owners. Arzo was always quick to get involved in new social circles that came his way. While we were on a six-month temporary assignment at the Johnson Space Center in Houston, Arzo impressed Erasmo and me profoundly by hanging from a lamppost at his first Mardi Gras street party in Galveston and throwing beads at hoards of young women whom he effortlessly converted into a brand new pool of like-a-good-time girlfriends. He followed that up the following year center stage on a Mardi Gras float in New Orleans. Back in LA, Arzo started going to 'exclusive' lingerie parties in Hollywood initially as part of the photo crew then as chief photographer. He had no background whatsoever in photography, but he always had the best pictures.

Arzo and I were both in Texas for Saint Patrick's Day in 1994. Arzo had rented a limousine for the evening to drive him and the many new friends he was sure to make from bar to bar in dee-luxe style. He had given the chauffeur a beeper and a list. The list paired numbers (coded 1, 2, 3, etc.) with bars (addresses and phone numbers included). The concept was simple: Arzo would call the beeper number and enter a code. The chauffeur

30

was to drive to the matching location and pick him up. That way he was free to go anywhere (with anyone, anytime) and still be able to summon his attention-getting ride with ease and efficiency and play that attention for all it was worth. I marveled at how *meticulously* he planned every detail and how *nonchalantly* he executed his plans. I was also dying to know the results of this particular grand design the next day.

Vincent de Cordoba: "Did you get any?....With the limo?"

Arzo: "I threw up in the limo."

Vincent de Cordoba: "Did they charge you extra?"

Arzo: "No. I did it in a cup. I did it very elegantly."

Another memorable character I worked with was Carlos Barata. Carlos was Columbian, from New York. He walked with his chest sticking out and his gelled head cocked back defiantly, like he was looking at the ceiling. His use of profanity was so natural, it sounded right. Whenever he inhibited it (not to offend certain genteel individuals or while making formal presentations to large groups of people), he didn't look happy. Carlos was also one of the best engineers on the program. He was famous for working very hard, putting in long hours and managing a heavy work load. As with all great leaders and individuals who's involvement made a difference, Carlos knew how to laugh at himself. I had damaged my knee playing soccer and was scheduled to undergo orthoscopic surgery in a few days. Carlos had heard about it:

Carlos Barata: "Where are you going [for the knee surgery]?"

Vincent de Cordoba: "Oh, [HMO X]...over here..."

Carlos Barata: "I know the doctors personally. They came over the border with me."

As I write this book, I wonder which quotes and which characters will emerge as each reader's favorites. Why mention that now? Probably because I am about to introduce Hugo Mountain, who may be my single greatest inspiration for collecting all these quotes and writing this book. Hugo Mountain was a giant of a man. Two hundred and eighty-nine pounds (131 kilos). His smallest finger was larger than most thumbs (and probably some wrists). He wore coke-bottle glasses, and his breathing was audible to even the hard of hearing. A veteran of the aerospace business, Hugo Mountain had worked on numerous projects before coming to Space Station. He had seen it all before. Although he was characteristically cynical about everything, Hugo was fun company. Jose Cabesagrande and I never missed a chance to learn something wise from him or capture one of his eternal quotes.

One morning, in the early days of the project, Hugo Mountain stopped by the office I used to share with Jose Cabesagrande before I became the manager of my team. He had just returned from a trip to somewhere near San Francisco where he had gone to see his elderly mother who had suddenly taken ill (something pretty serious - like a stroke). We were all concerned, and we hoped everything was alright under the circumstances:

Jose Cabesagrande: "How is your mom, Hugo?"

Hugo Mountain: "Her mouth works."

3.1.2.5 *Documentation*

I never really fathomed the term 'documentation' before working on the Space Station project. Once I began working in the aerospace world, I heard people say things like, "By the time this thing is ready to fly, you'll be able to stack the documents from here to the moon - seriously!". Like any sane newcomer, I thought they were exaggerating at first. Sadly, in time, what they said grew truer and truer.

Some of the 'engineers' on the project fell into the twilight zone of the documentation world, never to emerge. They passed paper around and made endless changes to existing documents. They held hundreds of telecons (conference calls by phone) to talk about changes. They sent out 'change pages' for review and comments, and then they all got together somewhere to conduct 'spec reviews' and 'lashups'. Comments were reviewed, one at a time, and changes were either rejected or approved by a series of review boards. The outcome? New documents (Revision X+1...).

In the front section of any proper aerospace document is a section called 'Applicable Documents', which lists all other documents affecting, or affected by, that document. So changes made to any given document usually flow down from higher-level documents and must be 'flowed to' peer and lower-level documents.

That then leads to the need for 'traceability' (which, for any given requirement or design element, is a specific trail back from a design detail to a justified origin, the driving requirement). The history and connectivity of the meaningful content of these documents is 'managed' by traceability matrices, which are basically spreadsheets full of pointers (up, down and sideways). Inevitably, however, elaborate schemes such as this are an irresistable invitation for major problems to arise. The documents are always inconsistent with one another and lagging behind the real design and the real hardware and software (out of date and out of touch with reality).

The smart people didn't waste too much time with the documentation. Borrowing the term from a documentary film classic that should be familiar to some of the more literary readers, the smart people used 'double-secret' tactics to buy the time needed to do the real work. One such tactic was the trusty old stand-in dummy:

"They did the same thing we did - they had a bogus traceability matrix."

-Archie D'Arc

As long as the traceability matrices existed (pages and pages of coded numbers and acronyms), the people who made their living monitoring the compliance of others with respect to too many inflexible rules and standards were content. They filed their periodic reports without 'findings' (official term for a non-compliance, which is a problem), and went back to their normal routine of attending the occasional meeting here and there and reading a report once a week. Nothing too demanding. What was actually *in* the traceability matrices didn't mean much until everything settled down at the end and the design details were flowed backwards to adjust the requirements for compliance with the design. It is important to note that engineering integrity was never compromised. The requirements - the real and sacred requirements - of crew safety and sustained vehicle functionality were seared onto the brains of everyone in the critical path. We lived them - and suffered for them - every single day. We may have taken a few liberties with the documentation in the early days, but we *never, ever, ever* compromised the design or the hardware and software for our Space Station.

Back to the documentation. 'Book Manager' was the title given to the 'stuckee' (the person stuck with having to do something) assigned the responsibility for getting a document produced and delivered on schedule. Book Managers usually coordinated a team of writers (the term is liberally applied here) who contributed the text, tables and figures that made up the document. Book Managers had to deal with assigning sections of the book to revolving-door writers with inconsistent abilities who contributed generously to society's ever-waning command of English grammar and vocabulary. They also had to contend with dirty looks and delays from the photocopying, or repro, department ("bad/poor planning on your part does not constitute an emergency on my part" was a popular sign at many a repro service organization). The amount of effort it took to get those books out was, for healthy minds, mind boggling. I would never have accepted so miserable a job. That's why I intentionally kept myself as ignorant as possible about book management - to make sure they never assigned it to me. This well-known (and underappreciated) deficiency of mine increased my reliance on far more patient men like Peter Gallant:

Vincent de Cordoba: "What's the figure number?"

Peter Gallant: "You don't go beyond four levels for a figure."

Vincent de Cordoba: "So, what's that?"

Peter Gallant: "2.1.3.3-3".

Vincent de Cordoba: "You're a genius!"

Peter Gallant: "No, I'm managing a book."

Peter Gallant was a model professional. He was a capable engineer, always willing to do what was asked of him, never making a fuss about the glaring absence of allure that may be the star quality of a particular assignment. We were both on short-term assignment in Texas for a few months, and we worked with each other on a daily basis. Peter, who sported what most people would call a military-style haircut, always wore a smart shirt and tie, neatly pressed khakis and Florsheim shoes - even when the Popular Largeness people (our customer) established a much more casual dress code (at a minimum, no ties).

After prolonged exposure to the Resistoglide crew's irreverent attitude (which, I can proudly say, shared more than a little similarity with that of characters Hawkeye and Trapper from the TV series, MASH 4077), Peter Gallant, though retaining his haircut, finally took off the tie and began to wear jeans. Eventually, he even began to partake in equally-healthy vices such as our 1994 World Cup betting pool (where he placed second in winnings) and a popular gentleman's club off I45 on the way to Galveston. And he still did a good job on his document.

The cleverness of the documentation system is that it is naturally perpetual. I looked up after my first few years on the project, and there were thousands of different Space Station documents all over the program. There was enough work generated by the changes alone to keep a whole lot of folks busy enough until retirement - many different retirements, year after year. On top of that, new documents were being generated every week.

Occasionally, however, we did receive heartening news of some restraint in the face of such uncontrolled expansionism:

Endora Broome: "The Mode Team chairman wanted his own document for FDIR [Failure Detection, Isolation and Recovery]."

Jose Cabesagrande: "Then he wanted his own capability. They didn't even give him that. All they gave him was a subparagraph."

'Mode Team' was a term that came to us from the Space Shuttle program and was promptly misapplied to any cross-disciplined team of people tasked with wrestling with the nebulous. Endora Broome was a member of my [not mode] team for a while. She put in long hours at work and was extremely committed to the safety of the Space Station. Her favorite word was 'inhibit' (a technical feature that inserts an extra, precautionary step before activating a given function or command that could potentially be hazardous). Endora was (in)famous for her ability to mesmerize her audience (especially some of the older gentlemen who so loved to listen to, and look at, a [definitely] charming young [for them] lady) whenever she was in danger of losing any technical argument. The trick was not to look into her eyes. Whenever she tried casting her spell over the people who knew her best, she would inevitably start to laugh at herself as soon as we began smiling and telling each other to avoid eye contact with her.

Organizationally, the greatest merchants of documentation hailed from the Systems Engineering and Integration (SE&I) departments. They controlled all the officially-but-not-in-actuality-important requirements documents that were eventually filled out and modified - long after they would have been useful - to comply with the as-built hardware and software. Those people took themselves very seriously. Others looked upon them as lightweights:

"SE&I will write a paper two inches thick. They'll end up saying, 'There is radiation. There is plasma. And you'd better be careful.'"

-Hugo Mountain

As mentioned earlier, the specifications produced by the SE&I organizations across the program were, more often than not, ignored by the design engineers. We designers thought the specs were too general; basically useless. This lack of respect led to one innovative suggestion for restoring the battered image of the SE&I documentation community:

"We should add a standard clause at the back of every spec that says 'And we really, really mean it!'."

-Jerry Bonanza

Jerry Bonanza was a long-time SE&I veteran who got out of SE&I after a few years on Space Station but continued to encounter the same spec problems with the subcontractor he later had to manage. I admired him for still being able to recognize, and make fun of, absurdity (if only in a melancholy way) after being exposed to it for over twenty years.

Technical people (*genuinely* technical people) were often irritated by the forces of documentation to the point of speaking out publicly without reserve. Joe Bob Anderson was one such person. Joe Bob worked on the software for the Space Shuttle Main Engine before I recruited him to join my team. He was a 6'7", no-nonsense engineer who understood the most complex levels of software design and had the experience to back up what he was building for the Space Station. He knew the difference between how things were supposed to happen and how things really happened. He concentrated his efforts in the realm of reality and had an open disdain for those who did not. He especially disliked wasting time on 'metrics' (performance measurement data, plotted to show status and trends for reporting to management):

"First of all, those that count 'shalls' are weenies."

-Joe Bob Anderson

Individual requirements imposed on the flight hardware and software were usually expressed as 'shalls'. The Software Requirements Specifications included statements like "The [name of specific software program] shall (tracking number) collect the [specific data] from the [specific source] at a rate of once per second".

All this documentation formality causes as much, or more, trouble than it is designed to avoid. There are 'shalls', and 'shall' numbers, strict document format regulations (established by the Department of Defense), rules for numbering tables and diagrams, rules for making changes.... When everyone is increasingly sidetracked into arguing about all these inconsequential and trivial documentation details instead of getting on with the real job at hand, frustration sets in. The following words, printed as they are on this page, years after they were uttered with dismay and in disgust, cannot possibly convey to the reader how infuriated one could get because of the documentation:

Vincent de Cordoba: "I don't know how they ever landed a man on the moon..."

Jose Cabesagrande: "Easy. They had no specs."

I always made my fierce dislike for overdocumenting everything to death public knowledge, avoiding worthless paperwork assignments in favor of doing what really needed to be done. On one occasion when we first began the transition from the Freedom program to the International Space Station program, someone suggested that I go to Huntsville (where the busiest activity was taking place) and support the effort, which, of course, featured....documentation:

Vincent de Cordoba: "I don't want to go down to Huntsville and sit around with a bunch of assholes discussing documentation."

Max Schwantz: "That's my life right now."

Max had just returned from there.

For the record, I am not against documenting obviously important information. That is good engineering practice in general. For a system as big as the Space Station, it is an obvious necessity. I only become upset when the number of people talking about documentation is large enough to hamper the people trying to get the real job done (trying to actually build something); when the amount of documentation eclipses the amount of hardware. The immortal Hugo Mountain summed up that situation - *our* miserable situation - sweetly:

"Of course we ship hardware. There's a staple in every document we prepare."

3.1.2.6 Telecons

Telecons [conference phone calls] are a convenient way to communicate simultaneously with others around the country or around the world without requiring anyone to travel anywhere. Telecons enabled a number of Space Station engineers in different locations to talk with one another simultaneously and work through the issues of the day. The only drawback (or benefit, depending on your perspective) was that the people at all these different locations couldn't *see* one another.

Full-blown meetings were conducted regularly via telecon, complete with agenda and presentation charts that were Faxed out to the attendees who would be 'tying in' (connecting). Presentation copies often did not get Faxed out to anyone until the actual pitch (presentation) was under way, and it was not uncommon for some sites to receive their copy after the presentation was over (which, on occasion, made trying to follow the presentation a bit comical, if not a total waste of time).

Telecons always began with a phone ringing in a conference room or someone's office. After the caller and receiver identified themselves and verified the connection, they would often activate their respective mute buttons while they waited for everyone to be connected to the network and for the stragglers to show up. Occasionally, the waiting period invited a little sparring-session warm up just for fun:

Vincent de Cordoba: "Resistoglide!"

Skip Vroomberg: "So what? Are you on the speaker phone?"

Vincent de Cordoba: "Yeah, and at least on ours you don't have to use tape to hold down the mute button -"

Skip Vroomberg: "Nice *building* you work in..."

Vincent de Cordoba: "I'd rather be working in a dump like ours than be *laid off* from a really nice building like yours!!"

The SGT Space Station folks worked in a much nicer building than we did. It was seven stories high, with lots of shiny marble, metal and glass. It had 360° of spectacular views, including the mountains around the LA basin and the Pacific Ocean. Though our SGT colleagues complained that their cubicles were small, they did enjoy modern office furniture (post 1960's was all they would have needed to come out ahead of us). I recall that they even had marble in their bathrooms. Our bathrooms had signs on the doors that read "Please No Newspapers".

Our building at Resistoglide was basically a two-story, cement airplane hangar with no windows. SGT had smooth, modern elevators. We had a single freight elevator that we couldn't use. Our office furniture was mostly over twenty years old, and our bathrooms, with the exception of the executive crapper, were, frankly, an embarrassment. And on top of all that, we used to bake in the summers because we were in the San Fernando valley and our 30-years-of-service air conditioners only worked in the *winters*. This was explained to me once by Resistoglide's air conditioning repair guy, who used to stop by regularly in the summer. He said something like the air conditioners work by blowing in the air from outside, and, when it gets as hot as it does in the summer, they simply overheat. You get the picture.

Skip Vroomberg was a close friend of mine who worked for SGT. He was smart and dedicated. He also talked at a hundred miles an hour. He hailed from Iowa (like Captain Kirk, he used to say) and spent some time repeatedly barely pulling off technical presentations to air force generals in St. Louis before joining the space station program. Skip worked hard – like us - and knew how to laugh at himself, as did we. He was a key member of a small network of people that I trusted and could count on.

Seasoned telecon veterans always came prepared with other work to do while the telecons dragged on. They also knew how to make full use of the marvelous mute button to go 'off line'. Most of the time, telecons were painfully drawn out and exhaustingly boring. Fortunately, the lack of visual feedback enabled people to go off line for extended periods of time without penalty. Sometimes, during telecons that lasted all day (over eight hours - seriously!), people could put the phone on mute and leave the room for hours, no problem. The trick (not so much dependent on skill as on luck) was not to miss anything important.

Off line was also a safe and familiar place to go when someone asked too difficult a question (difficult either because one is not prepared to answer and needs help or because the subject or answer is politically or contractually hypersensitive). Being off-line and providing no response at all was a good way to buy valuable time. Another trick was to have someone else chime in for you and say, "[the key person] just stepped out".

The mute button also contributed to the sanity of those of us with a heart rate greater than zero, stuck listening to slow-motion people richly lost in their own confusion, in that it encouraged some hidden comic talent to emerge and entertain others without fear of losing one's job:

Jeffrey Sprinkler (talking to all on the telecon): "By the way, the definition of 'failure' *does* exist on this program."

Lou Alfrito (*on mute*): "We've set new standards."

Jeffrey Sprinkler was the takes-himself-far-too-seriously Chairman of the FDIR Mode Team (he was also the principal inspiration for a delightful little literary work of underground comedy written by Carving Bear). Lou Alfrito was an old-school old man. His productive days of writing software were well behind him. With getting the points he needed to retire from Resistoglide being his primary goal, Lou Alfrito's most valuable contributions to the organization those days were occasional cynicism-based zingers like that one.

We were all so used to listening to you-are-getting-sleepy presenters and lambasting madmen on these telecons that the rare appearance of a moderate professional was very much appreciated and worthy of a compliment:

Vincent de Cordoba (on mute): "This guy's reasonable."

Wiley Method (in same room): "Relatively speaking, he doesn't sound rabid."

While I am heralding the versatility of the mute button with these accounts, it should be noted that the mute button is a powerful tool that needs to be handled with some care. If one forgets to mute and blurts out some albeit deservedly derogatory remark, everyone connected to the network (including the direct or indirect target of the remark and all their evil friends) is going to hear it. One time, I erroneously believed we were on mute and regrettably revealed - loud and clear - to all the other participants around the country how thoroughly engaging the whole discussion was for Jose Cabesagrande and me:

"Where are we going to lunch, Jose?"

Presenting new information for the first time over telecon occasionally shocked the target audience into startling the presenter. This happened to me one time when I was reporting on the results of one of our earlier efforts to reduce the number of Ada (the software language we used) source lines of code (SLOC) in our system. As part of a program-wide software scrub activity, we had to cut down on the number of lines of code ('scrub' was the popular term for painful reduction of SLOC, sensors, computers, control functions, weight, power, ...you name it). Our customer then was the Director of Software at NASA LeRC in Cleveland, the passionately careful Don Carlo.

Don Carlo was a likeable character though he was invariably complaining about everything, like an eternal victim. He used to fly to Cancun annually for margarita-assisted beach therapy and always returned very dark. As a general rule, he wanted to be respected, and he was worried about having to report our results to *his* bosses at NASA Level II the following week (he dreaded making any presentation to those guys).

I began to state the quantitative results of our most recent software scrub to Don Carlo:

Vincent de Cordoba: "There are now 62,300 EPS Ada SLOC, of which the RSVP [a key EPS computer] has 24,800."

47

Don Carlo: "HOLY SHIT !!!"

Justifiable concern at that time. Long after Don Carlo and LeRC were off the Space Station program, the actual number of SLOC eventually wound up being very close to that estimate and fit within the computing resource allocations. But, at that moment, when Don Carlo responded like he did, the only thing to do was hit the mute button.

3.1.2.7 Meetings

As someone who has suffered through some exhaustingly nonproductive meetings over the years, I am encouraged by my ability to still admit that [brief and focused] meetings are sometimes necessary. When many different people are responsible for many different parts of the whole job, meetings can pull them together to facilitate the exchange of information and reinforce the common goals. Meetings can be an efficient way of getting something useful done if they have a clear purpose defined and they are conducted with some degree of order and alacrity.

They can also be a criminal waste of time when they are conducted without a plan, an agenda or an effective moderator. The Space Station project certainly had its share of that type of meeting. The people who called those meetings were often trying to complete a milestone or resolve a problem that, if neglected, would have had some dire consequence on somebody (usually the person who called the meeting). The people they invited were the people they thought could help them do the work or solve the problem. Sometimes they also had to invite official, auditor types to attend (sit in the room, contribute nothing, have a doughnut, nod off for a while...) because their stamp of approval was, incomprehensibly, required for validating the meeting.

Many people invited themselves to meetings. They were Professional Meeting Attendees. They went to meetings, picked up the handouts and then wrote some kind of report or letter to justify their existence until the next meeting.

And then there were the Doughnut Eaters. They were very selective about the meetings they attended. They appeared exclusively at meetings that had free doughnuts. Their standard routine was to walk into the meeting, grab a couple of doughnuts, stay for a few minutes (at least long enough to eat them) and then get up and leave, grabbing another doughnut or two on the way out.

Most people who were not Professional Meeting Attendees or Doughnut Eaters obediently attended all meetings they were invited to and sat through each one until it ended. Many of them took notes in their [Franklin] Planners (large and trendy - almost mandatory - appointment books), mostly to schedule new meetings. In certain cases, this got out of hand:

"I just go from meeting to meeting. I don't have time to look at my planner."

-Jerry Bonanza

Jerry Bonanza demonstrated that he was still able to ridicule the system with statements like that. But while he cheerfully complained about going to so many meetings, he still went to them all. To counterbalance that automaton-like behavior, there were a few rebellious individuals who abhorred meetings in general and avoided them with vehemence. Not because they were afraid of having to interact with other people, but because they felt that the real work was done by capable individuals, not by committees or boards made up of incompetents. They categorized the workforce into 'do-ers' and 'talkers', and talkers went to meetings. One of the greatest do-ers I ever worked with, Marcus Electricus, said this:

"I'm very suspicious of anything called 'design' that happens in a meeting."

It would be difficult to convince someone like Marcus Electricus to agree, but, occasionally, meetings were important. *Very* important. Sometimes we had to attend to defend ourselves against opportunistic scoundrels making a frontal attack on our design and our organization. A situation like that usually came about when some disgruntled individual at NASA or a competing contractor, upset about the fact that their design or ideas had lost out to someone else's, incited a gang of troublemakers at one of the program's partner organizations to challenge the baseline design (the one the disgruntled guy lost to) and propose a better alternative (with the ultimate goal of snatching the business away).

The attacking organization would then put together a huge presentation and go around the country, pitching it to everyone and trying to gather support for an overthrow. The defending organization was almost always the last to see it. The motivation for the contractors was always to keep the money flowing in. Money meant jobs. More money meant a good chance of promotion for the rainmaker. Less money meant layoffs. The motivation for the disgruntled loser was usually revenge, mischief, or an obsession with forcing his way on the world.

My team was always ready for battle (we had to be or we would have never been able to defend anything long enough to get it built). On one strange occasion, a team from one of our own sister organizations (same company, different division) was coming to tell us their story on why our control architecture was no good and how their alternative was better. This story had already been presented to everyone else, including our NASA

51

customer, LeRC. In the tradition of Hannibal gathering intelligence about his Roman opponents prior to using it against them in battle, we learned what we needed to know before the showdown:

"I know all these guys [from the sister division] - none of them are geniuses."

-Max Schwantz

Max was right. We were prepared. The battle took place. They lost.

3.1.2.8 Presentations

Building the Space Station, it turned out, required a huge number of presentations. *Thousands* of presentations. Presentations are a vital part of aerospace industry culture. With thousands of people building a single vehicle, communication was imperative. The most common method for exchanging ideas, soliciting endorsements and providing general information was making a presentation or pitch. There were different sorts of presentations, usually based on the reason for having to make the presentation:

Requirements-review and design-review presentations described, to some degree of detail, the characteristics of the system being reviewed. The presenter would systematically proceed through the system's component subsystems and stimulate one of two popular responses from the audience: agitation or narcolepsy. These requirements/design-review presentations substantiated popular lamentations that the whole project was based on 'viewgraph engineering'. Viewgraph engineering is a process by which the design of the vehicle to be built is proposed piecemeal, in the most general of terms, on charts which change every day. What the real engineers desperately needed instead was to capture the system and all its necessary details in proper engineering documents so the vehicle actually had a chance of getting built.

Frontal-attack presentations (introduced in the previous chapter) were where one mischievous individual or group would go after another group's design/product/contract by inflating any existing problems and presenting their tarted-up alternative (which was no surprise to anyone but the profoundly oblivious). These presentations went well beyond upsetting the group under fire. As soon as the charts were pitched, word would get back to home base, and defense measures would be launched. The attacking organization usually didn't have many friends to begin with (or it would have been less insecure and busy working on something constructive), and, following each blatant attempt to discredit others, that number almost always went down. Frustration sometimes led to astonishment and disbelief when a given issue which was decisively closed was allowed to be reopened again and again by the disgruntled loser who was trying to replay a Superbowl that was lost convincingly two years ago (and three years ago, and four years ago, and...).

Come-back-from-the-dead presentations bravely fought back frontal attack presentations and recaptured lost ground for the time being (until the enemy regrouped and tried again). These presentations featured technical counteroffensives to restore the confidence of others in one's design after someone else had mocked it, as well as impassioned closing arguments to justifying one's existence organizationally. Come-back-from-the-dead presentations were understandably the hardest to have to make and pull off:

"You know what's funny? Every time it sucks, I gotta present it."

-Carlos Barata

No matter how bleak the situation seemed before the pitch, Carlos usually succeeded. That's why he kept getting assigned tough jobs like come-back-from-the-dead presentations over and over again.

A more common type of presentation were the *status presentations*. They basically summarized the current achievements and issues for managers who needed to report something to their management on regular basis. 'Metrics' (the measurable progress indicators such as the number of such-and-such completed versus the number scheduled) were what management wanted to see. As metrics-based management became the rage in the mid-nineties, these presentations that were supposed to measure progress dominated the presentation scene. They also, pathetically enough, severely hampered the progress of the real work. As the project's managers and administrators increasingly outnumbered its do-ers, the demands for more metrics and more frequent presentations of the metrics got worse and worse.

Talking about progress became more important than actually making progress, and making progress suffered as a result. Fittingly, metric-based management was its own worst enemy because the data were always manipulated to make everything look better than was really the case. That gave senior management a false sense of security (maybe it would be more accurate to say a lessened degree of concern) and led to things getting a lot worse before they had to be corrected. Shame on those damage-causing conformists who went along with the metrics charade (never having to pay for their acquiescence), and cheers to all the do-ers who got the job done anyway.

One useful type of presentation, in terms of assisting progress rather than hampering it, was the *trade study*. Trade study presentations assessed a handful of candidate options for solving a problem or choosing a specific design implementation to meet a given requirement and, most of the time, recommended the one to pursue. After the assessment was presented to the peer group, a management decision to go with one of the options allowed the engineers to move on to the next step. Trade study presentations usually included a statement of the issue, evaluation criteria, options considered, some sort of quantitative assessment of each option and a conclusion and recommendation. Pretty straightforward. Argue a bit about the data for a while, then make a decision.

Salesman presentations tried to impress potential new customers with what had already been achieved with the Space Station project enough to get them to shell out some bucks for a spin-off product or service. Most of the time, these presentations *did* manage to impress their audiences. The trick was to convert their interest into a tangible contract, and that was much harder to do (but not impossible). A variation of the salesman pitch was the *educational* presentation, where the provider of some system or equipment to be used by the rest of the community would try to explain what it was and how it worked. In this case, instead of going after new business, the presenter was simply looking for acceptance of his or her technical product as a legitimate part of the existing contract:

Vincent de Cordoba: "How did your presentation go?"

Cyrus Koobideh: "It was good.....alright......who cares..."

Most of these presentations could be designed to be made at one of three basic 'levels', depending on the seniority of the target audience: top-level, middle-management and technical. Effective presentations were always tailored to the right level.

The top level was for the big bosses. They had to deal with hundreds of issues, so there was never enough time for all the details - just the bottom line. A lot of the engineers never figured this out, but Julius Dusenberg had an efficient way of reminding them, as Floyd Crawdad pointed out to me one day in Reston during a major state-of-the-project pow wow that was running well behind schedule:

"These guys [NASA's top managers] need to adopt the Dusenberg method. After [the presenters] get past the first chart, you say 'OK, what's the fucking point? Why am I sitting here listening to this bullshit?'."

Floyd Crawdad was a senior manager at NASA LeRC who, unlike most senior managers, got into (and definitely understood) the technical issues in great detail. He was also well read and a classy addition to any worthwhile conversation. Floyd Crawdad had a mercilessly dry sense of humor which I very much missed when he left the project to revive a dormant writing career and make numerous trips to Madagascar.

The middle-management level liked a bit more detail. They liked bar graphs and summary tables, and they wanted just enough detail to keep them versed in the use of the buzzwords (trendy terms for the popular themes of the day that only fashion-conscious industry lightweights ever adopt). If the presentation issue was big enough, the middle-management level was always a necessary step to have to take before having to make the pitch to the top level. A significant cost in energy all around. Naturally, and in full accordance with certain well-known laws about the flow of information from the bottom of an organization to the top ("...it is strong, and it promotes growth") , the real message rarely got through.

First-line management and the core of the engineering workforce operated at the third level, where the real

57

message was painfully clear and presentations got into as much technical detail as necessary. This level often got carried away with the details, gradually wearing down the opposition and putting to sleep the undecided and the close-to-retirement, and often wound up achieving the main objective.

"You know you're in for a bad briefing when the guy comes out and says 'Well, the magma poured forth, and the continents were formed...', and, by that afternoon, you're up to Maxwell's equations."

-Hugo Mountain

The success or failure of these presentations depended heavily on the presenter. Boring, unenthused, monotone people gave boring, unenthused, monotone presentations. Hyperactive, mad-scientist types (like Skip Vroomberg) got distracted easily. They darted all over the place and, distanced themselves further and further away from their point (if they even had one to begin with) and customarily lost their audience. In the case of Skip Vroomberg, he usually had a point. His trademark handicap, however, was showing his extremely detailed 'before' and 'after' charts (including his most famous 'before' chart, the mesmerizing *Space Station on Drugs*') and going off in all directions in pursuit of a hundred competing thoughts.

"This is probably a Skip Vroomberg chart...and another characteristic is he's probably not even talking about it."

-Julius Dusenberg

Everybody knew Skip Vroomberg was enthusiastic by nature, and his presentations were expected to be lively. Marcus Electricus was also enthusiastic (he was truly passionate about his work, *and* he drank a lot of coffee). He didn't present as often as Skip Vroomberg did, but that did not deter him from setting a new standard when, in a fit of child-like excitement prompted by indications that the NASA bosses who had requested a special presentation on his sophisticated electrical data filtering algorithm finally began to understand it, he climbed up onto the table. Such a novel spectacle demanded some swift, yet discrete, intervention by his manager, yours truly:

"Marcus, you're going to have to get off the table."

Presenting was an art - part innate, part practiced. Most of the time, audiences were very demanding, even hostile. That meant presenters had to be well prepared, confident and quick on their feet. The perfect presenter in my opinion, and the opinion of many others, was a gentleman named Gary Speaker. Gary Speaker prepared well. His charts had structure and were easy to read. First, he told his audience what he was going to tell them. Then he told them. Then he told them what he just finished telling them. Classic. Furthermore, Gary spoke slowly and deliberately, making sure everyone in the room understood everything as he made point after point. His pauses were sometimes uncomfortably long, but Gary knew what he was doing. In the end, everyone was focused, the issue was clear, and Gary usually got what he wanted (as long as his pitch did not threaten the political agenda, of course).

Presentation preparation followed a general pattern most of the time. An event would occur where the reaction would ripple out (and down) to the poor soul who had the action to put together a pitch (most of the time, the person would also present their pitch, but sometimes the pitch had to be prepared for someone more senior to present). A rough outline was first developed, then filled out. The content had to be accurate and supportive of the main goal of the pitch. Backup charts that went into deeper levels of detail were always a good idea in case more detail would be necessary. Sometimes (in the dominant fire-drill mode) the pitch was due the next day (and maybe in Houston or Cleveland or Reston, Virginia). Other times, there was plenty of time to prepare and revise and tweak and 'massage'.... For the more important presentations, the final draft emerged only after a series of taxing reviews with middle management. A fair amount of time was spent on fine tuning the charts, and editing and re-editing could go on for days. The point here is that a lot of a priori effort usually went into a pitch.

Jerry Bonanza prepared such a pitch once, and he was sent to Reston to present it. The senior program managers chairing the meeting were so underwhelmed with the presenter directly before Jerry on the agenda (who had given his organization's pitch on the same subject) that they decided to delete the next two agenda items, including Jerry's pitch.

"I spent four days making charts that were never pitched. I want to go home."

-Jerry Bonanza

During the entire time I worked on the Space Station project, I only had two mentors; Julius Dusenberg and

The Captain. I rarely got to be around Julius Dusenberg. The Captain was one of the founding members of my team, and I was fortunate to have him around almost every day.

The Captain really knew his stuff when it came to system design. He understood control systems, computers and software inside out, from top-level functional design down to bit-level (lowest details) implementation. The Captain was an ex-fighter pilot from Viet Nam who survived being shot down three times over the jungle. He also knew, and taught me, a few things about life based on Eastern philosophies and his personal experiences that helped me get through some difficult times.

Most of the people we worked with found The Captain hard to understand. He thought it was because English was his second language. I think it was because they faked their way into positions for which they were not qualified with bogus credentials (smart people never had any trouble understanding him). The Captain almost always had some difficulty with his presentations for two reasons: (1) English was not his native language, and (2) his knowledge was orders of magnitude deeper than that of most of his audience most of the time.

On one occasion, one particular 'aggravationist' (the aerospace equivalent of a soccer hooligan) and self-appointed language critic (who insisted on making it known to everyone that he was more proficient at his native language, English, than a non-native) incessantly pestered The Captain with interruptions that analyzed and challenged every phrase, for which he received this silencing reply:

"Don't read my lips - read my brain."

-The Captain

Sometimes presentations provided a perfect setting for breaking off diplomatic relations. When people attacked one another in public, the coming-out animosity usually lasted a long time after that, if not forever. Lucas Buffet was the likes-to-remind-everyone-about-it chairman of the FDIR Mode Team. The FDIR Mode Team was supposed to define all the possible failures that could occur on the Space Station and what to do about them (for example, if the such-and-such computer fails to respond to commands and refuses to relinquish control of the subsystem it manages, then the control system should shut off the power to it and switch to the backup computer). One problem with the FDIR Mode Teams was that they spent most of their time (years) defining terms like 'hazard', 'catastrophic', 'inhibit' and 'interlock' and generalizing everything to breathtakingly advanced levels of uselessness instead of defining concrete situations and recovery actions that would have been useful to the system designers.

Max Schwantz was one of those system designers (on my team) who quickly realized that these guys were not going to help him or anyone else. He was smart enough not to need their help. He was also smart-*ass* enough to publicly proclaim their ineptitude by repeatedly referring to their work as "nebulous" whenever he got the chance, like the time Lucas Buffet was presenting some FDIR stuff to a technical audience in Houston:

Lucas Buffet: "You know, you keep using that word [nebulous], and I think it's just to piss me off!"

Max Schwantz: "It's working."

Presentations were serious business most of the time. That's why we made fun of them before, during and after. Harry Silvers and Carl Stevenson were two profanity-free, always-positive nice guys with bigger-than-average families. Harry Silvers hired me into the Space Station project and was my first boss. Carl Stevenson was my second boss before he gave up on managing our team and Harry asked me to take over. Rico Sambico was a forty-year old father of two who looked like he recently graduated from college, and he told us raunchy jokes as though he were an excited teenager. He also did a smooth impression of Sammy Davis and taught me how to snarl my upper lip and talk like Al Pacino in 'Scarface'.

Harry Silvers: "People [at the Restructure Design Review] like the fact that this group [the Control System Design Team] can keep a sense of humor about it."

Archie D'Arc: "Jose's fly -"

Carl Stevenson: "Jose's fly was open ?!?!"

Rico Sambico: "He needed a pointer…"

To ensure that the requirements for the Space Station's systems were right and that the design satisfied those requirements, we conducted design reviews. These reviews were held for the customer and anyone else who had an interest in the system or component under review (such as those who interfaced with it or those who had to operate it). As part of the formal deliverable process, there were Preliminary Design Reviews (PDR's) and Critical Design Reviews (CDR's). PDR's were supposed to make sure that the requirements for the system or component under review (a) existed and (b) were 'flowed down' correctly (meaning that they were properly derived from higher level requirements). CDR's were supposed to make sure that the design (the architecture, functions, subfunctions, inputs and outputs - down to the lower-level details) complied with those requirements. If so, the go ahead was given to proceed with implementation (to build it). If not, problems and issues were identified, and a delta CDR (or follow-up CDR) would be necessary to make sure all those problems and issues were ultimately resolved.

At PDR and CDR, everyone gets to take shots at *your* system, *your* requirements and *your* design. You are expected to answer all the questions and defend your system. Understandably, the customer would be a little nervous, if not visibly upset, if you didn't know your system (although sometimes certain individuals who lived for the downfall of certain others were outwardly delighted). On one such occasion, the most senior NASA visitor at Resistoglide's Electric Power System PDR, Sid Gould (a small, astute man of quiet demeanor who wore dark shirts and gold jewelry), struck out at the most senior

Resistoglide manager at the review over his weak response to an important technical question:

Sid Gould: "...and saying 'I don't know' is just not good enough [at PDR]."

Rusty O'Tool, our boss - so awkwardly under fire at that moment - was a weathered old pirate who had a black belt in karate and drove a faded old Porsche 911 Targa, filled with cigarette butts and yellowing newspapers. The newspapers were there "to protect the dash", he used to say. He was thoroughly divorced and always on the prowl. On more occasions than not, I heard him offer to walk a woman employee over to the nurse's station if he heard she wasn't feeling well, yet I can't seem to recall him ever showing the same concern for any of the men. Pre-political-sensitivity-era guy. Straightforward approach.

Here he was, challenged in public. No face-saving, partial-credit way out offered in the attack. As all of us froze with discomfort. Our fearless leader thought for a couple of seconds and then broke the nowhere-to-hide silence with an ambitious response that caught his accuser off guard:

Rusty O'Tool: "What is it we don't know?"

That PDR did not end well.

As a matter of PDR/CDR procedure, if anyone objected to a document, drawing or data table that was under review, they wrote and submitted a 'RID' (which stood for Review Item Discrepancy, was pronounced 'rid', rhyming with lid, and was basically a formal issue sheet). A RID would basically state an issue with the requirements or the design and suggest a specific corrective action. RID's were collected and categorized by topic or subsystem. They were then reviewed by subteams, according to category, and each was 'dispositioned' (either approved 'as is', approved with modifications, withdrawn by the author, or rejected by the review board). When the subteams had dispositioned all their RID's, the top-level RID board was convened, and each of the subteams presented their results (*this many* RID's dispositioned, *that many* approved 'as is', etc.). A RID author who wished to appeal the rejection of their RID by a subteam could do so at the top-level RID board. If they succeeded, they got their RID approved (most likely with modifications). If they failed, they got their RID rejected. A second time. For emphasis.

The contractor usually got the OK to proceed with the design, or the implementation of the design, at the conclusion of PDR or CDR, respectively, with the provision that the approved RID's be incorporated within a specified amount of time (usually forty-five days). This was not always easy.

Jerry Bonanza: "How do these actions generally get closed."

Harry Silvers: "The person at [NASA] Lewis dies."

Successful PDR's and CDR's indicate that a basic level of stability has been attained on a given program. The muddier the picture at PDR or CDR, the greater the number of RID's. If PDR's and CDR's are conducted before the requirements are well defined or before the design is developed to meet the requirements, RID's are bound to flow forth in large quantities.

Jose Cabesagrande: "It's a funny time to have a CDR."

Max Schwantz: "Any time on this program is a funny time to have a CDR."

Another reason to acknowledge the achievement of those who still succeeded in building this space station.

Less-than-successful PDR's and CDR's usually led to talk of having to go back and do it again (*'delta'* PDR's and CDR's). The customer would be unhappy with the overall state of the requirements and/or the design, and, after hundreds of hours of preparation time, tons of documentation, special logistics (hotel and restaurant maps, dedicated conference rooms, additional phones and computers) and lots of doughnuts, they would want another review. Thanks to the principles behind the old saying, "put your money where your mouth is", full-blown recurrences of such extravaganzas were minimized.

"If they [NASA] expect another PDR, or 'Son of PDR', they're going to have 'Son of Funding' too."

-Hannibal Ferguson

Hannibal Ferguson was a Resistoglide Vice President and the Program Manager (top boss) for our part of the Space Station contract (which he was also credited with capturing). He was a New Yorker. He was the opposite of a frail man, and his size and stance were testament to over thirty years in the aerospace industry with a proportional number of visits to his favorite restaurant in Houston (the little Italian restaurant with the unlikely name that is home to the best lasagna on this planet, as far as I'm concerned). He was knowledgeable about military history, and, overall, he was a good general for whom to work and from whom to learn.

Regardless of the technical or programmatic outcome of these formal reviews, we were guaranteed to be entertained by how ambitious they were, the material under review, the politics of the day and the personalities. No one was ever more entertained than Carving Bear:

"This review is not as much a circus as the last horizontal integration review was. Can you believe this?!?! We actually get *paid* to come down here [Houston] and do this!! I mean, for this kind of entertainment, we'd have to pay *thousands of dollars!*"

And with the following words immortal, Hugo Mountain reminds us that, eager as we may be to let go with some fitting reproach, striving for correct language is always good form:

"Is 'peckerhead' hyphenated? I'm writing a RID response."

3.1.2.10 Traveling

Working on the Space Station project imposed a lot of business travel on many of us. *Years* of business trips. *Hundreds* of meetings. Different locations across the country, as well as outside the United States. It quickly became routine to fly back and forth across the country just for a meeting. I used to drive to LAX (Los Angeles International Airport), park in the C Lot (cheaper, long-term parking), go straight to the gate (never checking in any luggage), change planes in El Paso and Phoenix (a feature of the cheapest fare to Houston), take the shuttle bus to the rental car lot, get in the car and program the radio station settings, drive to the meeting, go to dinner with the group and then finally check into the hotel late that night - all on auto pilot.

The organizations that made up the Space Station program were made up of people who traveled and people who didn't. My only objection to that perfectly logical division of responsibility was that the people who processed the travel expense forms for those of us who had to travel never actually traveled for the company themselves. All the rules. None of the hardship. As if to strain an already unsympathetic relationship with an obvious guilty-until-proven-innocent overtone, the non-traveling employees in the travel-expense-form-processing department were known as 'Travel Audit'. Imposing and impersonable.

Travel Audit began with the general assumption that anyone who was traveling, or had just returned from a trip, must be getting away with something. Their job was to catch those somethings and deduct the corresponding dollars from the crook's reimbursement check. They looked at the hotel. Most recognizable business chains were far too luxurious. What was wrong with the Roadside Inn? They looked at the plane ticket. Non-stop flights were much too extravagant. So what if we arrived at the meeting a bit drained and bedraggled? They never accepted the bit about needing to be alert and making a good impression. 'Suspect' flight departure and arrival times drew regular questioning. If someone wasn't leaving at, or before, the crack of dawn and returning past dinner time, they were more than likely getting away with some illicit leisure time. Rental cars had to be midsize and shared. Meal receipts were checked. The amount of effort spent in scrutinizing and arguing over all the details of all the trip reports cost so much more than the dollar or two that Travel Audit was trying to recover here and there that reason eventually overcame absurdity, and Resistoglide switched to a simpler, per-diem system based on destination.

The undisputed champion of running into trouble with (and giving a fair share of trouble back to) Travel Audit was Z-Man Habibi. Z-Man was a charter member of Resistoglide's Flight Software team who was later promoted to Manager of the team. The heart of Z-Man's prickly relationship with Travel Audit was that he was an incurable gentleman who had a soft spot for the finer things in life (he drove a Lexus, wore a Gucci watch and drank Courvoisier). Z-Man liked to stay in decent hotels, and he didn't mind paying the difference above the per-diem allocation himself in order to do so. He believed that, as a businessman who was traveling to a meeting to represent the company, he deserved to be able to take a non-stop flight at a reasonable hour. He also regularly paid an extra couple of bucks out of his own pocket to rent a full-size car. Consequently, Z-Man's expense report always got attention.

On one business trip to Houston, Z-Man needed a ride from the meeting at SC all the way across town to Houston Intercontinental Airport (he and I were sharing a rental car and I had to stay at the meeting). He called around to get the cheapest rate for a taxi. The first place wanted $65. Too much. He tried a couple of other numbers. He managed to find a taxi that would take him for $42, and he left. Unluckily for him, the name of the taxi company was something like 'Clear Lake *Limousine* Service'.

When Z-Man submitted his expense report back in California, the travel auditors zeroed in on the word 'limousine' and made a major issue out of his blatant self-indulgence. Z-Man tried to explain, but they doggedly wanted to nail him for their trophy cabinet. After weeks of arguing (which cost a few hundred dollars more than the disputed dollar amount), I believe they settled on a partial reimbursement. The story got back to Houston, and, the next time Z-Man was there, Bud Hellcat couldn't resist teasing him a bit:

"When does your limo get here, Z-Man?"

There were certain constants we all experienced in making so many trips over the years: screaming babies on the plane, peanuts (by the half-ounce bag), tired rental cars, rain (floods were not uncommon), musty hotel rooms, wrinkled shirts, badging problems getting in to the NASA centers and contractor sites, successful meetings, disastrous meetings, boring meetings, worthless meetings, sustenance by vending machine, long days, happy hours and big group dinners. It was not uncommon to travel across the country, on occasion, for no detectable benefit whatsoever. Sometimes agendas changed. Sometimes we went in case such-and-such happened, and nothing happened.

Dutch Williams was a senior SC manager who was assigned to work the Space Station contract. He was a big man with big character, and he had an instantly-recognizable laugh (extreme exhale, strained large red face, steam-whistle noise coming out of his ears). Dutch was never far from the underlying fact of the matter:

Dutch Williams: "You came [to Reston, Virginia] all the way from the West Coast just to have a drink with Hellcat?"

Vincent de Cordoba: "That's the sad truth..."

'Sad', not because Hellcat was an unworthy drinking companion (au contraire, amigo), but because there was no other outcome from the whole trip. As I recall, that evening in Georgetown was a superlative one. We had a fine dinner with Carlos 'The Gangster' Barata, and then we went bar hopping. By the time all the bars began to close, we were best buddies with all the bouncers and had met or observed a more-than-adequate array of entertaining individuals for one evening.

When dinner and a drink at a bar fell short of reviving one's ever-wilting appreciation for the basic joys of this life, there were always the 'gentlemen's clubs'. These uncomplicated establishments advertised "food, drink and girls" - exactly in the reverse order for why their customers went there. I often wondered if anyone really thought that the morality police would fail to notice the 'girls' part if it were mentioned at the end, after 'food' and 'drink'. It must be so, as every town on the business circuit had its gentlemen's clubs, and business thrived.

72

"That's one thing I've learned being a *NAS*-hole is that I've become a fine connoisseur of strip joints in multiple towns."

-Zack Buckshot

Zack Buckshot was an engineer who worked at NASA LeRC in Cleveland. He had more hours logged on a tractor than in a car, drank one kind of beer (domestic) and hunted his dinner in his back yard every evening. I was glad to see him making progress toward any kind of connoisseurship. As for all the charming and personable 'dancers' who told us they did it to earn money for classes at the local community college and for their little girl or little boy who was growing up without their dad, I sincerely hope that some of them actually succeeded in moving on for the better.

3.1.2.11 *Geographical Differences*

The Space Station project was already an international project long before they changed the name from 'Space Station Freedom' (SSF) to 'International Space Station Alpha' (ISSA) (changing the name of a problematic entity is an effective, though paradoxically obviously weasely, tactic for distancing oneself from a publicly-recognized problem). ISSA added the Russians to the original team of Americans, Europeans, Japanese and Canadians. The name was then scrubbed down to just plain 'International Space Station' (ISS), which stuck. The geographical and cultural differences, mixed with the rules, regulations and bureaucrats of government programs, provided the right ingredients for some very funny moments.

The international differences proved to be, more or less, what any multi-culturally-aware person might expect. We Americans were the least formal of all the project partners and the quickest to open up with what we thought and where we stood. American style derives much of its character from the bold participation and uninhibited opinions of the individual. Students in American school systems are encouraged to speak up and interact with (not just listen to) their teachers and to make presentations to their classmates. Americans are not shy.

Texans are a convincing example of this. Since the NASA Johnson Space Center is located in Houston, Texas, Texans naturally made up a significant percentage of the American team on Space Station. They wore cowboy boots (really; with suits, even), drank beer, ate steak, and assumed the driver's seat as far as the project was concerned. You bet.

The Russians were a lot more guarded. It was a strange thing to be working with them; to be in technical meetings with real Russians, with their authentic Russian-English accents, in Houston. They were visibly affected by the radical contrasts between their transmutating world and all the abundant and flashy Americana to which they were suddenly exposed. A single dinner bill in Houston often exceeded the monthly salary of a degreed and experienced engineer in Russia. That quickly put a serious expression on everyone's face. The Russians were more fond of their vodka than beer, but, either way, after a few vodkas or beers with us, they were an affable lot to socialize with.

The Europeans were a mixed bunch - English, French, Italian, and German, for the most part. They wore Euro-intellectual clothing ('droopy-couture'; no sharp edges) and were used to their own, European business etiquette (such as profound levels of restraint and unhurried lunches with wine). They were usually outraged by something or other that NASA (= the Americans) had changed without informing them. This was not an unreasonable reaction since the potential impacts (costs) to the Europeans were often in the millions of francs or deutschmarks. I often wondered how they coped with being a junior partner of a people who's cultural sophistication comes across to them as an oxymoron.

The Japanese shared a similar frustration. They were very serious and always wore serious (dark) business suits. When one of their bosses would arrive at Houston Hobby airport or Houston Intercontinental, his people would go to the gate to greet him (bowing, in suits all) and take him to the hotel. Deep respect and formal protocol, characteristic of their culture. They probably thought that the entire Space Station project was completely undisciplined and totally out of control because of the way things were run in Houston.

Communication was another problem. The Japanese often projected puzzled looks while they struggled to translate insightful Texan phrases like, "Shit, son, betting the whole goddamned farm on a pair of threes is like being up shit creek with no paddle and stepping off the boat. I mean, you ain't exactly got a first down inside the ten. You're just putting lipstick on a pig, boy!" Before they could even begin translating, they had to first ascertain some word recognition out of the valuable insight that was just thrust upon them - "Sheee-yitt, suhhn, bett'n thuh hole gaahdddainged farm ohwn-uh payrr-uh threes is laaahk bein' uhp shihtt creek with no paddle an' stepp'n off the boat. Aaaah muhyyn, you ain't egg-zakkly gotta furst daah-yown insaaahd the teyhn. Yuhrr jesssputt'n lipstick ohwn-uh peey-yig, boaah!" I must point out, however, that after an oratory like that, the puzzled looks were not exclusive to the Japanese.

Personally, I didn't have enough interaction with the Canadians to record anything of note. I'm sure they too noticed the cultural differences inherent in such an international project and they brought a piece of Canada to the party.

Although the international differences were often the most striking, domestic differences were equally engaging. The Space Station project was so big that almost every US state had some piece of it. That is why meetings were held all over the country, and there were so many occasions for people to visit and host their colleagues from other states.

I once attended a Software Design & Architecture Team (SDAT) meeting held in Huntsville, Alabama, for which the seasoned members of the SDAT had flown in from Texas, California, Massachusetts, Virginia, and Arizona. During the meeting, we got to discussing loading the flight software into the flight computers as part of the critical initialization process of the avionics (flight control) system. The term 'I-load' was commonly used for the initialization load (or first-time, startup load) of the software, and Carving Bear was deep into a discussion of some scenario or other which necessitated such an I-load, saying:

Carving Bear: "...a new 'E'-Load -"

Sam Ewing: "You mean *'I'*-Load?"

Carving Bear: "I-Load! The reason I said *E*-Load is for *'E'*-nitialization."

Sam Ewing: "You Alabama guys talk funny."

The Japanese should derive some special satisfaction out of the fact that Sam Ewing is a Texan.

Southern accents were not the only ones that managed to charm so many eyebrows up and down as the listeners struggled to recognize the strange words they were hearing while they leaned back with looks of mystification and marvel. The Boston accent could easily accomplish the same.

I, myself, had lived in Boston before moving to California, so hearing a pure Bostonian accent was, for me, as comfortable as telling Archie D'Arc to smaaahten up and order the chowdah. Some people didn't exactly feel the same way and often poked fun at the native Bostonians. The most characteristically Bostonian retort I ever heard to such reckless provocation came from an SGT engineer named Joseph Revere, who returned to his beloved place of origin not long after silencing a pack of Californians who were deriving a little amusement at the expense of his Boston accent:

"The next time someone from the west coast is laughing at how someone from the east coast is talking - where did the pilgrims land? *Marina del Rey* ???"

-Joseph Revere

Whether it was the soundness of Joe's logic or its stunning elusiveness, silence prevailed.

Aside from cultural traits and accents, the food varied from place to place. Houston had the best food in my opinion (and Z-Man's and Jose's and Erasmo's and...). Houstonians (the whole family) dined out more nights than not, it seemed to me. Visiting business people dined out *every* night. The food was generally excellent and the portions large. Gulf shrimp and other seafood, steaks (monster cuts), Tex-Mex, Cajun, Italian... Los Angeles certainly had good restaurants (filled less with families than with all the 'beautiful people' 'in the business'). LA, by far, had the widest range of ethnic groups and food types (sushi/Japanese, Thai, Mexican, Chinese, Vietnamese, Korean, Italian, French, English, Irish, Brazilian, Spanish, Peruvian, Indian, Iranian, Armenian, Lebanese, Hungarian, Scandinavian, Russian, Moroccan, In-n-Out Burger...) plus plenty of great salads and pizzas whose creatively combined ingredients define Californian cuisine. I did not go on any business trips to Europe (Cleveland and Houston were more likely), but the universally acknowledged excellence of French and Italian cuisine does not need my endorsement. I wonder what those guys (the French and Italians) thought about the Thai chicken pizza?

The weather was also another differentiator between all the different places that were home to all the people on the Space Station team. Russia, Canada, Cleveland, and Boston were mostly cold. Los Angeles and Phoenix were warm and dry. England was wet and cloudy. Reston, Huntsville, Japan, France, Germany, and Italy could be cold or hot, but not as dry. Houston was volatile. It was humid (always). When it was hot, it seared your skin. It even snowed once in the winter of 1993/4. Most of all, it rained (poured might be more accurate). More than once I heard accounts of my business colleagues having to abandon their rental cars in the middle of Houston's I45 freeway while on their way to the airport and wade, waist-high in water, to safety beyond the access road ("What, you too?!?!!!").

Vincent de Cordoba: "We come to Houston so often, let's buy a house down here."

Carving Bear: "Why would I want to buy something that's going to float away?"

3.2.1.12 The Customer

At the outset of the Space Station project in late 1987, Resistoglide was on contract to the NASA Lewis Research Center (LeRC) in Cleveland, Ohio. The project was named 'Space Station Freedom' (President Reagan's jab at the Russians before anyone dreamed that they would one day become a partner on the project). LeRC and Resistoglide together comprised what was called 'Work Package 4'. Popular Largeness had a contract with the NASA Marshall Space Flight Center (MSFC) in Huntsville, Alabama, and together they formed Work Package 1. Work Package 2 consisted of Stylish Glass Towers on contract to the NASA Johnson Space Center (JSC) in Houston, Texas. At the earliest stages of the project, there was also a Work Package 3; Major Bulbous, on contract to the NASA Goddard Space Flight Center (GSFC) in Greenbelt, Maryland. Work Package 3 disappeared early on, leaving Work Packages 1, 2 and 4 to be managed and coordinated by an exclusive little NASA entity known as 'Level II' headquartered in Reston, Virginia.

In 1993, the management structure of the Space Station project was drastically reorganized to avoid almost certain termination. JSC was given total control of the project, and Popular Largeness (Seattle) was named as the single Prime contractor. Stylish Glass Towers, Popular Largeness (Huntsville), and Resistoglide all reported to Popular Largeness, Prime Contractor.

Most of my noteworthy records of interaction with (or around) the customer come from the Freedom days. There are two reasons for this. The first is that the early stages of the project required a substantial amount of interaction with the customer (at that time, NASA) as all the vehicle's requirements had to be established, and detailed roles and charters of all the participating organizations needed to be defined. As Space Station Freedom (which was mostly a struggling, fragmented, paper design) gradually metamorphosed into the International Space Station (which could boast real hardware and software that had to be perfected under the threat of real schedules and tightly-controlled budgets), engineers who were responsible for building the flight articles spent less and less time with the customer. At that point, what needed to be done was clear. What the customer cared most about then was the schedule and the budget.

The second reason I have more records of NASA, not Popular Largeness, as our customer is based on a fundamental difference in their two cultures and how they operated (how they did business). Popular Largeness, one of the most successful companies in the world, was deeply enamored with *processes* and teams. They spend a lot of time making charts (mostly bubbles and arrows) that layed out in look-how-hard-we-must-have-worked detail (way beyond sensor accuracy, incidentally) plans to produce plans. The result? Lots of process definition and administrative homogeneity but not a lot of individual distinction. NASA, on the other hand, more than made up for its academic (less organized) operating style with some noteworthy individuals (as one can imagine).

Case in point: LeRC's Don Carlo. Don Carlo's personal style contributed to the enrichment of his organization in its role as our customer. He was usually troubled about something or other, and he was never able to contain how he felt for very long. During one particularly tedious meeting where a well-beaten-dead-horse argument was still dragging on over which on-board system should have to calculate the correct secondary (beta) rotary joint angle positions needed to point the solar arrays at the sun from the station's vector (direction) to the sun – the Guidance and Navigational Control system (GN&C) or the Electric Power System (EPS) - Don Carlo exclaimed:

"For the amount of time and money we've wasted arguing about who should calculate the beta angle, EPS, GN&C, or even ECLSS [the life support system] could have done it by now. I'm beginning to think the only solution is that EPS gets the angle, GN&C gets the vector, and the Japanese get the money to build a new box to go and do it...so I can go to Japan."

The words of a justifiably frustrated civil servant, conceding to an accomplished people who have a reputation for getting the job done and exposing his underlying desire to travel to their country for free.

As Don Carlo was readily agitated, Bud Hellcat was bold. Hellcat worked on the Space Station with a personal style and charisma that blazed straight ahead like a 4x4 ripping through a pebble beach. He held some pretty senior positions at NASA relative to his age (late twenties, early thirties) because he was smart and he took charge. He was also confident enough to acknowledge his mistakes with a big ol' grin whenever he screwed up. Andy Mulligan illustrates this point:

"Hellcat's one of the few customers that I would call fucked up to his face."

Andy Mulligan was an extra sharp and dedicated SC engineer who had a scathing wit and could sniff out insincere people (especially technical imposters) in a microsecond. The eventual dissolution of SC's contract as part of the Space Station project did not sit well with him. As sure as there's a slice of lime in a cerveza con limon, he is still a little bitter about it today.

Continuing with the same basic theme of occasional underperformance, I remember being in a crowded meeting in Reston, Virginia, sitting next to Floyd Crawdad, who was the most senior representative from our customer organization at the meeting. Stylish Glass Towers (the Work Package 2 prime contractor under JSC) came under attack for something or other of its own doing. After two hours or so of scrutinizing SGT and making life painful for them, the big boys of NASA Level II shifted their attention to the other two Work Packages, 1 and 4. They wanted to know from MSFC and LeRC if their prime contractors, Popular Largeness and Resistoglide, respectively, had things firmly under control. When they directed the question at Work Package 4, Floyd Crawdad, having witnessed the chagrin of his counterpart at JSC (who was unlikely to have enhanced his career by poor management of his subcontractor) answered with some safe words, and the threat passed. I gave him a puzzled look, knowing that the words had sidestepped revealing the not-so-under-control reality. He whispered:

"Well, I couldn't very well say, 'You don't know how *fucked up* Resistoglide is'."

I understood later. What a clear thinker! What a team player! A smart man who knew when to bring up problems and when *not* to bring them up. He knew what our problems were. We knew what we had to do to fix them. There was no need to get dragged into the quagmire of the high-level, formal issue-tracking process - a move that would almost certainly drain us of the energy we needed to solve the damned problems. Floyd Crawdad was like a member of our family. He had earned the respect and trust of our crew at Resistoglide over the years. We never bullshitted him. Others were fair game:

Jose Cabesagrande: "Most of these numbers [estimates of computer processing speed and memory size] came out of the Data Management System User Requirements Survey, which is, as you know, an evolving changing dynamic static model."

Bill Hertz (LeRC Systems Engineering & Integration): "Uh......OK."

It all came down to respect. And we didn't just hand it out automatically, as too many people sell out and do, just because someone was our customer.

3.1.2.13 Unwieldy Project

The Space Station project was huge in every way. A huge undertaking. A huge space vehicle. It had to be. That's how it got funded. In order to sell the project to the politically-sensitive [really?!] United States Congress, the work was divided up and handed out to a number of states. And not just the states but other countries too. The strategy worked. By one of the most fundamental laws of physics, however, there was a price to pay (the cost of the lunch). The project was too big to manage with any effective degree of control.

In addition to the size of the job and the large number of players, the turbulence of the first six years owed much to the ineffectiveness and rivalries of the divided leadership arrangement. With three different NASA centers trying to run the show (each paired with its own prime contractor who, in turn, was teamed with its own gang of subcontractors to form the whole Work Package), NASA Level II had a daily obligation to exercise its role as coordinator and arbitrator. It did not do so. Problems just kept building up.

The three Work Packages and Level II thoroughly confused and annoyed the Europeans, Japanese and Canadians. They also thoroughly confused and annoyed members of their *own* organizations. There were power struggles within the work packages ("Your bosses *this week* are..."). There were also power struggles between the work packages (meetings called by one and ignored by another, covert and blatant initiatives by one to grab work from another, casual propaganda to discredit another based on past [non]achievements and present [in]experience...). And there were power struggles at Level II. Short-lived mutinies usually resulted in subsequent 'promotions' for the mutineers to positions of impotence like 'Director of Technology Research' or 'Program Manager, Advanced Initiatives') - not too unlike that Cheers episode where Woody's new title of '*Senior* Bartender' substitutes nicely for the raise he didn't get.

It's no wonder that NASA's international partners were upset most of the time. Not only did they have to deal with such chaos, NASA did not treat them as equal partners. I recall one incident where they were incensed to have been excluded from a meeting where the decisions made impacted them adversely to the tune of millions of dollars. It couldn't last this way, and it didn't. Don Carlo predicted;

"You've probably seen the last of the multi-work-package projects."

He was right. In 1993, the biggest reorganization of all took place to centralize control of the project. The Work Packages 1, 2 and 4 passed into history, and "Product Groups" 1, 2, and 3 (there's that renaming ploy again) emerged under a single prime contractor, Popular Largeness, who was managed by a single NASA center, JSC. This certainly did not eradicate all the problems (not least of which was how to actually design the vehicle and make it work), but at least it made it clear who had the authority.

Like me, some people naively joined the Space Station project to build a Space Station; to be part of building the modern-day pyramid. I say "*some* people", not all (as the reader might expect), because the project's workforce included plenty of people who couldn't care less [this is the correct way to say the phrase, incidentally] about building a Space Station. They would be just as content working on another missile program like the one they had just escaped from prior to being laid off. A job's a job. Keep a low profile. Only eight more years until retirement. Capice? One fellow I once interviewed for a place on my team told me the short commute was what appealed to him most about the job. I had asked him if he was a Star Trek fan.

The draining inefficiencies that oozed out of the management maze over the years, coupled with roadblock after maddening roadblock, gradually wore people down and chased them away, disheartened. Each person had their limit as to how many years of this now-bitter dream they could put up with. A few tough individuals managed to hold on by the teeth, maintain focus and stick with it just a little longer:

"I want to get this thing [the project] done and get outta here. You know, like a normal job."

-Marcus Electricus

Years went by. Very few people stuck it out. Most left, replaced by enthusiastic new blood to feed the cycle again.

3.2.1.14 Changing Requirements (What Does Everybody Really Want?)

Probably the most difficult challenge the Space Station engineers had to overcome (or, less ambitiously, had to not be utterly done in by) was the permanent volatility of the requirements. It is hard enough to design, build, integrate (between hundreds of organizations, national and international) and test all the pieces of a complex space station without having to deal with daily changes to the requirements. The requirements kept changing anyway.

After the deal was struck to bring Russia on as a partner in 1993/4, the entire assembly sequence (what piece connects to what, and when) of the vehicle was changed, the orbital inclination and altitude (which drive the required electromagnetic tolerance of the equipment) were changed, and the power, thermal and computer architectures were all changed. I'll stop there in recognition that the reader gets the point.

One popular method of NASA's used to achieve drastic changes in the design was the 'scrub', which basically entailed reducing the number of components and the overall functionality to wind up with less than before (less should be cheaper). During 'Restructure' (November 1990 to October 1991), scrubbing the flight computers was in. A lot of the functionality that was previously allocated to the lower-level, *distributed* computers to increase their local autonomy was pushed back up to the vehicle's top-level, *centralized* master Command & Control computers to justify reducing the number of computers allocated to each of the on-board systems. But when the new prime contractor, Popular Largeness, was given responsibility for producing the top-level Command

& Control computers, they recognized the overload at the top and pushed a lot of that functionality back down to what remained of the lower-tier computers *without* bringing back the scrubbed computers. Nice game. Tough technical problem to deal with. Costs money.

Whenever a specific requirement was not known, a placeholder for the unknown was established with the acronyms, 'TBD' or 'TBS' (To Be Determined or To Be Supplied). A couple of examples:

"The end-to-end response time for annunciating an alarm [sending a message] to the crew, from the time the alarm condition is detected to the time the [big red light and blaring horn] are activated shall be TBD seconds."

"In the event of a critical failure [as I said before, *years* were spent arguing over the definition of that term, and it's probably still being disputed...] in [System X], the computer responsible for [System X] shall perform the following actions: TBD."

The design engineers couldn't wait for thousands of TBD's/TBS's to be filled in, so educated guesses had to be made. Some times, the guesses were very close, and, when the specifics of the TBD or TBS were defined, the impacts (in terms of changes to hardware, software, documentation and schedules) were minimal. Other times, however, the guesses were off, defining the unknowns took years, and the impacts were significant.

Whenever the ground controllers at NASA wanted to add a function or capability to an on-board system to make their jobs more manageable, they sponsored 'change paper' (official documents that authorized changes) and pushed for approval. If the change was deemed necessary, and there was room to add it (the system could accommodate the added functionality), it was incorporated. If it was necessary, but there was no room

89

to add it, long arguments would ensue over what was to be thrown out to make room. If it was unnecessary (a luxury), and there was no room for it, it was dropped without a big fuss (for the time being, likely to reemerge in a year or so). If it was unnecessary, yet there was room to add it, it was equally likely as not that it be incorporated anyway until something important forced it out later (analogous to sitting in someone else's seat on a plane before takeoff). Since the definitions of necessity and luxury changed as the intransigent individuals who once fervently argued those definitions floated away to other, more leisurely jobs, the academic (paper) requirements were slowly overtaken by real designs, real hardware and real software.

If the hardware could not meet a specific requirement (based on feasibility), that requirement was deleted. The design engineers then had to compensate for the deletion with changes somewhere else (to other hardware, or to the software) that would still satisfy the original operational intent. Such moving-target circumstances effortlessly wore down and thwarted many an average engineer over the years (and less-than-average engineers within a month). The cleverest design engineers expected and prepared for this, however. They built their systems to withstand the changes.

A quick technical explanation is called for to appreciate the simplicity of Marcus Electricus' solution to a typical change in requirements. One of the major requirements imposed on the EPS was to always charge the station's batteries before going into the eclipse (or dark) period of the 90-minute orbit. This was because, during eclipse, the only sources of electrical power for the Space Station would be the batteries (there would be no sunlight available during the eclipse part of the station's orbit for the solar arrays to convert into electricity). The basic

90

algorithm (control logic) for satisfying this important requirement was designed to begin recharging the batteries with a considerable amount of electrical current upon transition from eclipse into the insolation (or light) period of the orbit. Recharging was to continue until the batteries got up to 100% State of Charge and then 'trickle charging' (continuing to drive a minimal amount of current into the batteries) was to kick in to hold them at that level. By design, trickle charging was supposed to begin a few minutes before the start of the each eclipse. The exact time was programmable.

Jose Cabesagrande: "Cad, Inc. [the subcontractor responsible for building the batteries] is telling us that the trickle charge requirement might go away."

Marcus Electricus: "So what? All we need to do is set the time equal to zero. Fuck 'em!"

The ability to adapt rapidly was (and usually is) essential.

3.1.2.15 Endless Redesigns

Hand in hand with the changing requirements came the endless redesigns of the Space Station. All the blame for the existing and projected cost problems that threatened to bring about the cancellation of the project by the U.S. Congress annually was always, and successfully, placed on the *design* of the vehicle instead of the management/organization where it mostly belonged. Consequently, so many efforts were undertaken to downsize the Space Station dangerously close to the point where its remaining capabilities and the value of the whole project could be seriously challenged. Each year, the project's top management would report on the simplifications and try to convince Congress that big savings would be realized. Plenty of people crowding the kitchen. No chef.

There were so many official redesigns of the Space Station that they all melted into one big blur for most of us. All kinds of special-purpose teams cropped up to fix problems they often outlived. It is important for the reader to appreciate that all this extra Alice-in-Wonderland-like activity required *real* support from real engineers in addition to all the different design reviews that are standard to the business. I acknowledge Jose Cabesagrande and his famous record-keeping ability for providing many of the following names and dates of some of the key events and gatherings that had the most impact on our organization, Work Package 4 (which later became Product Group 2):

- The Spanner Initiative, ~1989/90
  (changed power system from 20 KHz AC to DC)

- Work Package 4 (WP-04) Preliminary Design Review
  (PDR), 6/90

- The Turbo Team, 7-8/90
  - Sensor & Effector Scrub (reduced the number of
  data and commands)
  - DMS MDM Scrub (reduced the number of flight
  computers)

- The Restructure Team, 11/90-10/91
  - Software Scrub (reduced software functionality)
  - Control Architecture Redesign (simplified overall
  architecture)

- Mode Teams, 6/91-6/92
  - Integrated Avionics Mode Team
  - Command & Control Mode Team
  - DMS (flight computer system) Mode Team
  - FDIR/RM (fault management) Mode Team
  - Caution & Warning Mode Team
  - EPS Mode Team
  - Data Architecture Mode Team

- Mode Team Lashup Meeting, 8/91 ['lashups' were
  supposed to pull in and make sense out of all the
  uncoordinated parallel activities and meetings]

- Flight Software Requirements Review (FSRR), 3/92

- Software Safety Working Group (SSWG), 3/92-4/95

- WP-04 Restructure Design Review (RDR), 7/92

- Engineering Design Council (EDC), 2/92-9/93
  (produced the Technical Design Document, TDD)

- Software Data Architecture Team (SDAT), 2/92-9/93
  (produced the Integrated Avionics Software Design
  Document, IASDD)

- System Management Team (SMT), 2/92-9/93
  (produced the Avionics System Management Design
  Document, ASMDD)

- Program Data Architecture Team (PDAT), 2/92-9/93
  (produced the Program Operational Data System
  Architecture Design Document, PODSADD)

- PMCA/PVCA/MBCA Internal Preliminary Design
  Review (IPDR), 7/92

- Program Software Architecture Review #1
  (PSAR #1), 11/92

- PMCA/PVCA/MBCA Critical Design Review
  (CDR), 1/93

- WP-04 Critical Design Review, 2/93

- Program Software Architecture Review #2
  (PSAR #2), 6/93

- SPCA Critical Design Review (CDR), 8/93

- Transition from Freedom to International Space
  Station Alpha (ISSA), 10/93-3/94

- System Management Coordination Team (SMCT), 10/93-[?]

- ISSA System Requirements Review (SRR), 12/93

- ISSA System Design Review (SDR), 3/94

- PMCA/PVCA Software Requirements Review (SRR), 10/94

- Command & Data Handling Roadshows, 1/95-1/96

- Computer Based Control System Safety Task Team (CBCSSTT), 4-5/95

- Integrated Stage Software Specification Review (ISSSR), 6/95

- PVCA Preliminary Design Review (PDR) / Critical Design Review (CDR), 12/95

Repetitive. Years of re-evaluation. A huge amount of energy. A draining mental marathon to have to endure.

Each of these grandiose odysseys usually began with an official letter announcing that a special team was to convene somewhere (usually Houston or Reston), and all the organizations who received the letter would have to support it right away. The mission? To redefine, redesign, reallocate, re-specify, re-architect, re-debate, re-estimate and re-propose the whole thing. For the last time. Or else the station would be cancelled that year. Just like last year. And the one before that. And the one before that...

There were three categories of actor entwined in these tragic comedies: the current program management (who also commissioned the plays); the designated 'knowledgeable' engineers (sent to represent each of the affected organizations); and the rest of the folks back home (who kept working according to the *baseline* (old) plan until official direction was given to adopt the latest changes).

Carving Bear was regularly designated to represent his organization, Popular Largeness (Huntsville), when such support was required. After about the sixth or seventh time he'd been sent to brave one of these great spectacles, he began to show signs that his never-overwhelming-to-begin-with enthusiasm was possibly beginning to recede a tad:

"It's impossible, if you bring enough good people together, to get nothing done - but we're trying."

-Carving Bear

Larry Tosca bore the existence of at least one of the special redesign teams by looking on the bright side:

"By the way, our Station Management and Control Team - they've kind of gotten so ridiculous that they're fun to work with."

Not to be left out without making his contribution to the poignant skepticism, Hugo Mountain, in assessing the results of one of the more drastic of the redesign efforts, once lamented to Jose Cabesagrande and me about what he saw would be the eventual end product if things went on as they were going:

"We're going to go down to the Cape, and they're going to be soldering a monkey into a galvanized bucket with a flashlight."

At the time Hugo spoke those words, there were a lot more redesigns still to come (and go). Marcus Electricus understood that this project was like a Marathon and patiently accepted that it would take a long time for things to settle down while Max Schwantz put forth the mortgage-payment-based perspective:

Marcus Electricus: "They're still rearranging and reshuffling this project."

Max Schwantz: "We're still picking the meat off this carcass."

One of the classic authority figures at NASA, who presided over the Turbo Team, the Restructure Team and the Engineering Design Council redesign efforts, was the inimitable Barney Gruffmeister. Barney was as hardheaded as a cement cinderblock and had a habit of pummeling perfectly competent male presenters with an arsenal of expletives, pausing suddenly in mid-attack to say something like, "Excuse me, Diane..." in a polite, Southern tone if there was a lady in the room, and then snapping right back to continue the assault.

When Barney was enraged, no one else understood why. When everyone else was gravely concerned about something, he was usually in a great mood. Really great for morale. As the project struggled on, the redesigns got tediously old. Even Barney Gruffmeister expressed concern that yet another redesign so late in the game may not be the wisest use of precious resources so close to a time when the project was under its most serious threat of cancellation:

"It's like having plastic surgery at sixty."

It took over a decade (that's correct; ten years!), but the rate of the redesigns finally did slow down enough to enable the real hardware and software to start getting built.

3.1.2.16 *Proposals & Fact-finding*

Every time the mission and scope of the Space Station project were revised by a major redesign, and every time the customer (NASA, or Popular Largeness, when they took on the role of prime contractor) wanted to make changes to the existing design, contracts had to be modified. As you can imagine, the contracts that make up a multi-billion-dollar project such as the Space Station are complicated in pioneering ways.

I will gladly take the liberty of oversimplifying this subject, and, to this day, I'm deeply grateful to myself for never having learned enough about it to be recognized as good enough at it to do more of it. In short, the Space Station contracts followed timeless government/NASA rules about labor rates, equipment purchases, profit margins and incentives, allocation of subcontracts to small and disadvantaged businesses, etc. The contracts were mostly 'cost plus', which basically means that the customer pays for the cost of the work plus some fixed percentage (which defines the contractor's controlled profit). Each contractor broke the big job they were hired to do down into smaller tasks and provided estimates for the hours and material needed to do each task. The customer would then review the numbers, negotiate with the contractor over the number of hours estimated to do the work, and then allocate the actual dollar budget.

Every time any changes came around (a continual process), the affected tasks and budgets all had to be modified. This began at NASA and flowed down to the contractors, impacting different departments, teams, and individuals. As the manager of a team of engineers that produced specific products, I regularly had to generate and modify page after page of itemized tasks and hours scheduled through the year 2002. All the other managers across the program had to do the same thing. NASA was given a yearly budget. After they took good care of themselves, the contractors received their budgets, and that was then allocated down to all the smallest operating elements in the overall organization (like my team).

Contractual negotiations were a costly exercise repeated as often as possible. A wise old gentleman who'd worked at Resistoglide since before I was born and drove the same aircraft carrier of a car since then said, "It's just the usual; the government spending a billion dollars trying to save a million." The customer would send a team to Resistoglide and all the other major contractors for 'fact-finding'. Fact-finding was the operating term for the line-by-line interrogation of each team manager, questioning why they were performing each task, why there were so many hours for the task, how was the task different from a similar task being proposed by another team, etc. Down to smallest detail.

Some absurd things happened during fact-finding. For example, on one occasion, after the customer's 'fact-finders' (usually chosen for the job based on exceeding the requirements for certain social and psychological qualifications, preeminent of which is having no sense of humor whatsoever) arrived at the conclusion that another team (a purely-paperwork team) was claiming to be performing some of the same tasks that my team (a design/test/product team) was really performing, they zeroed out my team entirely (180,000 hours of work for the next seven or eight years deleted, nothing left).

After some carefully-chosen words convincing the customer not to shoot himself in the head, as well as a magnanimous admission by the manager of the other team that they basically got all their information from "the smart guys in the design team" (that would be us), my team was reinstated at about 90% of the hours we had asked for.

One reason we had that problem was the casual (as opposed to precise) use of the word 'verification', which appeared in the task description sheets of both teams. To establish a clear separation between the people who defined and performed the testing (which proved that the requirements for the system were indeed satisfied by the design as built) from the people who merely maintained the official checklist of that testing and the results for the customer, a clarification was needed:

'Ivan the Intolerable' (Resistoglide): "Well, what's your definition of a verification person?"

Russ Watson (NASA): "A verification person is basically a paper fairy that goes around checking off boxes."

Dr. Terry Memorable (Resistoglide; my team): "That's [the other team]."

Key revelations like that made all the difference. The outcome of these fact-finding theatrics could rarely be predicted with accuracy. Some managers prepared well and provided tons of data, yet their budgets were severely cut (excessive data was usually used to intimidate the investigators, but sometimes it backfired and provided them with clearer targets). Some managers did not prepare well, had only a few high-level charts and didn't do any meaningful work, yet, incredibly, they survived without a fight.

When it came to negotiating with the customer, the level of skill varied from manager to manager. Jerry Bonanza was a nice guy with a no-matter-how-bad-it-gets-I-can-come-up-with-something-darkly-funny-to-say sense of humor who liked to play bluegrass guitar in his other life outside of work. He wasn't comfortable haggling and was always a little nervous before the inquisition began:

Jerry Bonanza: "I know they could easily just kill me. I've never had a proposal I could justify."

Jose Cabesagrande: "But you got away with it with [NASA] LeRC!"

Jerry Bonanza: "They felt sorry for us!!"

Conversely, I recall one occasion when we used a highly evolved, straight-faced bullshit technique, combined with Ninja-like telepathic version of Curly's wavy-hand technique, to weave a good story for the customer and get approval for our estimates over the squawk box. The customer's response when we stopped talking:

"Hey that's OK with me...I mean I don't even know what we're talking about."

-Marty Wagner, negotiating $$$ with our skillful Resistoglide team

Marty was a likeable fellow, which is exactly why he wasn't the right personality type to excel at negotiation.

All the redesigns, proposals and contract changes eventually began to lose their tight hold on the attention of the people they affected. My boss at that time, Art Chartwell, who was our department head, was giving his team managers some guidelines during one of the later iterations of the redefinition of our contract when even his usually-effervescent interest level dipped just long enough to think about his retirement for a second:

"When we [estimate cost], [assume] the program goes out to 2004...Gee, I'm going to have 85 points [enough combined years of service and age to retire] by then."

-Art Chartwell

Art Chartwell never deliberately tried to be funny, but he certainly made us laugh a number of times over the years. An intelligent man, Art would often say amusing things unintentionally, and then laugh along with everyone else once everyone else began laughing - as if the hilarity of his own words had only then, for the first time, become apparent in his head.

If there is anything useful to be learned here from all this questionable   spending-lots-of-money-to-make-sure-no-one-is-overcharging business, it is none-other than the very civilized Floyd Crawdad who imparts upon us the cost-estimation technique of a master:

"When I put fat into a cost estimate, I do it so subtly, I don't even know it myself...because you don't want to stand up there with a guilty expression on your face."

3.1.2.17 Schedule Pressure

Schedules were a real joy to deal with on the Space Station program (in the most sarcastic sense of the word). Not because they were hard to meet (too much to do in too little time) - which they were - but because they kept changing and no one really knew what the schedule really was on any given day. We just worked as hard as we could, every day, to get as much done as possible before the forces of viscosity and arrestation got to us. The hope was that when all the automatic alarms inevitably went off in the plethora of independent and uncoordinated schedule databases that tracked thousands of scheduled deliverables, the delinquencies would not be too bad or last too long because everything was always being rescheduled when the difference between the planned schedules and reality became large enough.

To aggravate this thoroughly delightless situation, the project was totally schedule-driven. The pressure was always on to get a whole lot of work done in a short amount of time to meet some critical milestone. Upon getting a lot done but falling short of what was needed, the schedule would be redefined (translation: revised to annul the slip), and the panic would begin anew. It was like desperately trying to hurry up and build a sandcastle which keeps getting knocked down by the incoming waves on a beach, over and over and over and over...

The ironic thing about panic-based project management over the long term is that the project's duration eventually extends well beyond what would have been a manageable timeframe for getting the job done without all the fire drills. Everyone would have been much better off to have invested in systematic, steady progress from the beginning instead of counting on trying to hit the jackpot with a lottery ticket and changing the numbers every week.

Skip Vroomberg explained the Space Station project's perennial modus operandi this way:

"They didn't say 'Go out and do a thorough analysis and come back when you're ready.' They said 'Give us your charts on Wednesday.'."

The schedules were a bizarre game best played by a few crafty players. The referees were all the professional watchers of other people who did the real work. To play the game well was to meet all the milestones in some minimal, smoke-and-mirrors way without incurring any negative impact to the real progress being made. When official milestones were not met, there was so much extra work brought on by all the delinquency reports, independent investigations, repeated explanations, recovery plans, risk mitigation studies and organizational shuddering that the net result was often to unwittingly (maybe half-wittedly is better here) worsen the chances of getting the the original job done.

Archie D'Arc exposed his dread of the imminent when it looked like we weren't going to meet some milestones that we had already postponed more than once:

"We've got a lot of shit that's, like, on the verge of being extremely late."

Important milestones needed to be met. No question about it. And it's understandable if people got a bit excited when those milestones were missed. The bothersome thing to most of the few people who were actually responsible for producing a tangible product was that a significant number of the milestones were not that critical yet they automatically assumed an importance way beyond their true worth (when looking at the big picture) as soon as they found their way into all the redundant schedule tracking databases across the program.

Being able to officially postpone a non-critical milestone was usually an intelligent move. It allowed more time for making the proper preparations that would satisfy the requirements for meeting the milestone while simultaneously protecting the real progress from costly interruption. Often enough, postponing a milestone bought enough time for the milestone to disappear altogether as a result of bigger changes that rearranged everything. The trick was always to get the real work done in spite of the schedules.

3.1.2.18 Disenchantment Looms

Frustration levels on the Space Station project generally sagged up and down, somewhere between total dejection and mild depression at any given time. That should not be construed to mean that no one was ever happier than being mildly depressed - we desperately stole as much fun as we could out of all the politics, people and mayhem that richly characterized this ambitious project - but that the draining frustrations were always there, tireless, in the background.

One of my two favorite poets of eloquent disgruntlement, Hugo Mountain, felt a special calling to deflate any residual optimism at every opportunity:

Commenting on a typical the-best-thing-we-can-do-is-keep-working-hard pep talk from our Vice President (which always coincided with funding cuts and impending layoffs):

"Is our VP speaking again or is it just the Santa Ana winds?"

[For those readers unfamiliar with southern California's Santa Ana winds, they are seasonal gusts of hot air.]

Commenting on our company's policy for dealing with serious discontent in the workforce:

"When other companies see a sarcastic memo like this one, they figure the troops must be upset and they need to be talked to. *This* company wants to find the guy who wrote the memo and torture him."

Commenting on the Space Station project's careless habit of shooting itself in the foot and reloading over and over again:

"All is not lost, but we're closing the gap."

Commenting on blind obedience to the flawed rule that the customer is always right:

"We're the kind of contractor who'd bend over *forwards* for the customer."

Commenting on the fallacy that new things are always to be accepted as an improvement:

"You see, back in the 60's, you used to have to wait around for a printout because they were batch machines. Now, it's a 'Queued Print Server'. We've made a lot of progress..."

That other disgruntled poet, Carving Bear, once told me that each person goes through three stages while working on the Space Station program: (1) mad and frustrated, (2) depressed and frustrated, and (3) hysterical and frustrated. Well into Stage 3, Carving put aside his usual eloquence to reveal his frustration with the Space Station program's newest boss of bosses:

"Northfield ain't nothing but another goddamned lunatic in disguise."

Maybe Carving detected something I didn't, or maybe he was carrying over a wee bit of distrust which was richly fertilized by Brad Northfield's predecessors, but I liked Northfield. He took charge. We needed someone like him because he actually made decisions and got things done. For some reason, that made his bosses (the top brass at NASA who oversaw all of NASA's projects) extremely uncomfortable. For reasons masterfully circumvented in the official announcement, they didn't take long to get rid of him.

With such disheartening cloak-and-dagger skullduggery seeming to be powerful enough to go on indefinitely, Z-Man Habibi (who worked hard to be promoted to the physiologically-taxing job of Manager of the EPS Flight Software Development Team) blurted out one possible avenue to a less-stressful, more-profitable (if less-prestigious) way to make a living:

"Sell hot dogs in a good area - you'll make $10,000 a month............I'm serious!!!"

While Z-Man Habibi was dreaming about less stress and more money, Marcus Electricus expressed his disappointment in the organization that employed him, which, due to a pattern of poor decisions made by a clique of unqualified company lifers, hampered his efforts to get the right things done:

"I actually think Resistoglide is a fairly amateurish outfit to be associated with."

He thought so to the point of quitting to go work at SGT to do what he wasn't able to do at Resistoglide. When he came back to Resistoglide nine months later, Marcus

Electricus eventually realized his dream of completing his simulation of the EPS, and it received no greater endorsement than when we captured a contract to sell it to the people who were building the facility for training the Space Station's crew and ground controllers - the very same people who had built all the simulators used to train the astronauts since the Apollo program.

The great Julius Dusenberg was not one to hold back his skepticism when the occasion warranted it. Julius always asked designers tough questions, and, one time, he asked how we could be sure that the Space Station design was going to continue to work over a long period of time. One particular gentleman (I don't remember whom) offered him the reassurance, in earnest, that [company identity withheld; not even the dummy name used here] would be doing the maintenance on the vehicle. His reply:

"[That's] like going to a fucking shoemaker for open-heart surgery."

The smart people didn't have faith in much during those days.

3.1.2.19 'Organizational Excellence' (the Buzzwords)

Whenever organizations (military, sport, or business) rack up a less-than-impressive performance record beyond some tolerable time maximum, they are likely to undergo reorganization as the easiest action they can take to appear to be doing something about the problems. Reorganizations often seem to be successful at first. The most obtrusive problems of the previous organization seem to be solved, and the more faithful among the reorganized respond to the changes with reinforcing approval and commitment.

The skeptics, on the other hand, murmur their not-unfounded snippets of discontent. As time passes, the hidden problems of the new organization begin to introduce themselves (complying with the no-free-lunch rule). When the cumulative weight of all these problems combines with the realization by the head of the organization - or their replacement - that there needs to be a dramatic change, the organization swings back to where it came from, like a big, slow pendulum. And the cycle repeats itself.

There are many reasons why an organization is structured the way it is at any given time. The official reasons are things like matching resources to the tasks at hand, complementing an interfacing organization (such as the customer organization), and subdividing the different components of the whole job by function (financial, engineering, manufacturing, etc.). The underlying reasons, which are based on age-old human nature, are a little more entertaining because they include empire building, ass kissing, treachery, punishing the guilty, and revenge.

With major transformations taking place at the top, the contractors were continually scrambling to keep up. Resistoglide did its best to stay in the game. Concurrently, it wanted to preserve its status in a more efficient, global economy as a 'world-class' organization. The magic formulae? Continuous Process Improvement (CPI), Self-Directed Product Teams, Employee Empowerment, Taguchi Methods, the Company Vision,...Organizational Excellence (OE).

The fundamental concept behind all these highly-profitable-for-management-consultants ideas is to transform an inefficient, bureaucratic organization that is in danger of eventually collapsing into a lean and profitable operation that will survive the changing environment in which it is getting tougher to compete. Less people, no slackers, efficient processes, better results, more profit. The theoretical concept is fine. With respect (poor choice of word on my part) to all the efforts to realize that concept at Resistoglide and elsewhere, results, not surprisingly, seldom lived up to the expectations of the deluded and the deluding.

When the concept of OE was first introduced at Resistoglide, its value was questioned open-mindedly. People wondered why the company was going through the motions to adopt OE. At the let's-go-around-the-room-and-everybody-introduce-yourself-and-tell-us-a-bit-about-yourself beginning of the first of many mandatory OE classes for the managers, when it was Jerry Bonanza's turn, he made friends with the recently-converted, lightweight instructor right away:

"I'm Jerry Bonanza, Manager of Test & Integration. I'm concerned that OE has been, and continues to be,

112

disruptive, and I can't figure out what we're going to do here for three days."

The instructor (a human resource from the 'Human Resources' organization, which used to be known as 'Personnel' before they reorganized their name in accordance with the silly trend that gave America 'owner-operators' and 'chief information officers') answered something to the effect that people are naturally uncomfortable with change, and the class went on. For three days.

Whenever word of such concerns slipped by the censors and reached the ears of senior management, they were quick to offer their personal reassurances to the troops:

"A lot of people are really worried. I don't think they should be worrying. Look at this [OE] as if we're part of an experiment."

-Art Chartwell

A few of the individuals that had been hand picked by 'management' to be first in the organization to be taught the new ways and promote them to their colleagues occasionally showed encouraging signs of managing to retain control of their own minds:

Vincent de Cordoba: "Why don't you wear your 'OE? Ask Me!' button?"

Archie D'Arc: "Not my style..."

Archie D'Arc was open to new ideas without giving up the ability to think for himself. He never advertised his doubts *in public*, and, consequently, he was often tagged by senior management to participate on a series of special teams (referred to as the 'golden children' by some) that helped to elaborate and propagate new organizational concepts . Marcus Electricus was never asked to be on any of these teams because his views on how real business gets done were too well known:

"We don't need to do things right. We need to do the right things - by whatever method we can find!"

Shocking stuff.

Whatever the reality was for each individual affected by the OE pendulum, the official story would always be the same. The senior-management proponents of OE wanted to hear what they wanted to hear (all is well, the initiatives are working, no one is causing any trouble, etc.). Scott Howard, a junior-management proponent of not being bullshitted, who was fiercely dedicated to his team and had a talent for drawing convincing sketches of his colleagues, was never afraid to interject with his real opinion:

Art Chartwell: "Grady [the Resistoglide President at that time] wanted to get together and talk about the major successes of OE."

Scott Howard: "That won't take too much paper."

Much to nobody's surprise, Scott eventually got fed up and left to work back East. It was the gradual exodus of people like him that made it more and more difficult for the handful of dedicated individuals who remained and depended on the sense of humor of others around them to stay on.

Skip Vroomberg dealt with the OE pendulum at SGT differently. He understood the true essence of all these reorganization exercises. In keeping with Wiley Method's sound advice ("When the pendulum swings, duck!"), Skip ducked. But that didn't prevent him from doing his part to make sure no one around him was fooled:

"I have empowered you to do what I told you to do, Goddammit!"

-Skip Vroomberg

3.1.2.20 Layoffs

The aerospace business, as a lot of people already know, is no virgin when it comes to layoffs. Aerospace may have even invented them. Big projects hire and fire in bulk. They usually follow a funding-driven staffing profile that goes up steeply in the beginning, levels off for a while, and then comes down gradually back to zero over time. Laying people off also occurs as a by-product of reorganizations like OE.

When the Space Station project first started up as an all-out, fully-fledged contract, Resistoglide and all the other proposal-winning contractors were hiring with great commotion (it has even been suggested to me, on more than one occasion, that standards may have even been relaxed here and there to keep up with staffing targets). When the top of the staffing curve was realized, the reductions began.

Like lobsters in the tank at a decent seafood restaurant, the mood of the workforce was glum. There really wasn't anywhere to go for a lot of the people. The job market was down, especially for aerospace workers (who were thought to be beyond redemption by most people in the private sector who believed they were slow thinking, slow moving paper shufflers).

Hugo Mountain captured the general climate in his own, inimitable way:

The Captain: "Hey, long time no see! How are you, Hugo?"

Hugo Mountain: "I'm here this week, I guess."

Hugo actually survived many waves of layoffs, but, in the end, they got him. Although Hugo left for good, a precious few of his words of wisdom and wit have been preserved (to live on, fittingly enough, for a lot longer than some of the individuals who laid him off).

The layoff process was hard to get used to. Management had a tough job to do. When the layoffs first started, deciding who got laid off and who got to stay based on performance and projected project needs was, for the most part, a straightforward process. Due to the large number of people on the project and the hasty rate at which everyone was hired, many people were blatantly out of place and clearly not contributing (or even contributing negatively). It got a lot tougher after the obvious candidates for involuntary separation from payroll had been shown the door and most of the people who were left were doing a good job.

For psychological reasons, management was very careful about how much visibility they provided into any ongoing layoff. They tried to skirt around, or soften, the harsh reality when communicating about the layoff with the rest of the workforce. Clinical terminology was used to avoid the blunt words that might upset the troops:

Vincent de Cordoba: "I've been told that it's not a 'layoff', it's a 'reduction in force'."

Steve Black: "It's 'staff pruning'."

One of the flaws of 'staff pruning' is that it is impossible to follow the planned staffing profile exactly. Trying to get rid of exactly the right number of people at exactly the right time - which would be difficult enough in itself - doesn't do it. More specifically, and probably only understandable by those readers with a background in electrical engineering, the perfect solution (which is simply not feasible) would be a pulse-width-modulated reduction in people. So the reality for any given layoff was that either *not enough* people had been laid off to keep costs within the budget or that *too many* people were laid off for the remaining people to still be able to do the job.

Stan Buchanan was a big ol' veteran of the aerospace business who strained a Harley-Davidson on weekends and held various Space Station management positions at Resistoglide from Department Director (third-tier manager) to Team Manager (first-level manager) - in that order. Oscar Targa was a friend of mine who always told it like it was and had few friends as a result. They were experiencing the classic need-to-hire-people-after-the-layoff problem one day:

Stan Buchanan: "You know anyone who's out of work and looking for a job?"

Oscar Targa: "Yeah - how about the guys you laid of last week?"

3.1.2.21 *Farewell, Serious Contraptions*

One of the most visible casualties of the transition from Space Station Freedom to the International Space Station Alpha was the abrupt termination of the Serious Contraptions (SC) contract under Stylish Glass Towers. Capable individuals we had worked with for five years developing the on-board computer network management system for the Space Station were promptly reassigned to other projects around the country. Just like that.

Before they left Houston, Z-Man Habibi and I managed to get one or two dinners and lunches in with a few of these guys to say goodbye and cement the friendships we had established for future opportunities to see, and possibly work with, each other again. The SC guys were fond of a particular Mexican restaurant (possibly because of all the complimentary margaritas the owner habitually brought over to their table), so that's where we went.

Like the Delta Tau Chi fraternity brothers who had nothing more to lose after being kicked out of school in that informative documentary I referred to earlier in the 'Documentation' chapter, the SC boys were past the point of being concerned about any consequences. Andy Mulligan was the most upset, and he aired the feelings that most of his colleagues felt without reservation. They were outwardly bitter about having to pay such a high price while everyone else, arguably more culpable, was spared. It's not as if SC was the cause of all the problems for the Space Station program and all the other organizations had everything smoothly under control.

One of the many respectable qualities of Andy Mulligan was that, although he may not have agreed with the decision that booted SC off the program, he was still able to poke a little fun at the technical inadequacy of the

Prototype DNF Kit (a piece of software development equipment, hastily produced by SC and universally acknowledged to be a dud), the very first unit of which was purchased by a believing Resistoglide for a cool million dollars:

"Now that I'm off the program, I want to apologize for that."

Andy Mulligan could laugh at his organization's occasional flop against the redeeming backdrop of its history of successes. He was much harsher on the organization that ran the show in Houston; an organization that had experienced dramatic levels of success and well-deserved glory in the past but seemed to have waned of late:

"Most of the people at JSC - the thing that amazes me is that their brains generate enough electricity to move their legs. And that's really sad."

I learned a lot from the SC guys with whom I worked. I respected them for their technical knowledge, their extensive experience in the commercial computer business, their cutting sense of humor, and their professional conduct. It's a shame they didn't make it through to the successful conclusion of the program.

3.1.2.22 Design Issues

At this point in the story, I will assume that most readers have developed some appreciation, and maybe even a mild distaste, for the detracting environment in which we engineers had to maintain focus on the fundamental goal of the project - which was to build a space station.

The technical challenge was no cruise in the Caribbean. The vehicle was supposed to sustain human life in the harsh, unforgiving environment of space. It was supposed to snap together, piece by piece, in space, like a very big and very sophisticated LEGO toy. There were millions of parts, built by different contractors, all supposed to fit and work together without any problems.

Different people, tied down by their own, different experiences, have different ideas about how to do things. People also often quit the project before completing whatever it was they were supposed to be defining, designing, building or integrating, leaving the inheritors to figure things out for themselves. And, on top of all that, the lack of clear, stable and timely requirements only increased the number of possible design solutions, which led to change after change and worsened the ever-present schedule pressure.

One classic conundrum that haunted us, the design engineers, as we tried to design our flight systems was trying to find a balanced solution somewhere between what the users (the ground controllers and the crew) wanted - which was basically everything (total control, total data, all the time) - and what the system could do within the limitations of the components and the philosophy of keeping things simple to reduce the risk of things going wrong. Debates about this went on all the time, and no one was ever satisfied. The users wanted more. The engineers who had to build it (on schedule) wanted less.

Tim O'Reilly was a conscientious fellow who began working on the project while in his early thirties. Within a few years of working hard only to know more frustration than accomplishment, he was transformed into a grumpy and tired old man in his mid-to-late thirties. He was a thoughtful engineer (smart, as opposed to prone to making kind remarks to others) who listened to opposing viewpoints but did not have much patience with unreasonable people.

During one exhausting and unproductive technical meeting, the number of safety features (hazard-preventing interlocks, inhibits, backups, etc.) to be included in the design had been discussed to death. There comes a point where one has to stop adding 'safety' features [which, it can be argued, may actually *decrease* safety because they add complexity] to the design because the what-if-the-Nth-line-of-defense-fails argument can go on forever without reaching absolute certainty. With a reasonable agreement close at hand, someone representing the ground operations people still insisted that additional 'command inhibits' (extra steps which prevent inadvertent or unauthorized commanding by requiring two actions to take place before the function is performed) be built in. Tim O'Reilly had had enough and snapped back at the guy:

"If an astronaut forgets to put his helmet on before he opens the airlock,...Darwin works!"

Later, in that same meeting, the same disgruntled proponent of more safety features was trying a different approach by shifting the technical discussion into the realm of the English language, the requirements and the letter of the law. He was arguing that his scenario qualified as a credible 'hazard', as defined by the Space Station program, which opened the door for the inclusion of those additional, redundant safety features he wanted. Tim O'Reilly made known what he thought about that:

"If you use that [the Station program's] definition of 'hazard' in your house, you couldn't plug in an iron [without inhibits] 'cause it could be sitting on your head when you plug it in."

Most people agreed. Tim O'Reilly: 2. Other guy: 0.

I'd like to end this tale about command inhibits with the right perspective, if only to tease Endora Broome a bit. As I already pointed out, Endora was a dedicated engineer who strongly believed that a good, safe design required inhibits all over the place and resorted to her hypnosis-assisted charm to successfully convince others (mostly older men) and get them (the inhibits) into the design. The basic idea of command inhibits is to prevent a given command from being able to execute by 'inhibiting' (disabling) it. The inhibit must be removed before that command can be executed. Inhibits are applied and removed by other commands - which can, themselves, be inhibited. Woody Nelson, one of the most technically proficient engineers I ever worked with, once asked:

"What happens when somebody command inhibits the command inhibit command?!"

Since useful, detailed control system requirements were unavailable in the early years of the program, we, the design engineers, had to make decisions whether or not to include certain capabilities such as inhibits. Jose Cabesagrande explained this to Bud Hellcat during a C&C Mode Team telecon:

"The low-risk option was to put it [an inhibit] in there and make the inhibits inhibitable."

The war between the 'Safety Community' (which is what the inhibit seekers called themselves) and the design engineers went on regardless of individual skirmishes won or lost here and there. I do not exaggerate when I say that the Safety guys were still arguing over the definitions of 'hazard' and 'catastrophic' well after the hardware and software was running - safely - in the labs. No real engineer I ever worked with ever ignored safety (the concept). Real safety is a very serious business. It would be less than truthful, however, to pretend that the Safety Community (the cult) were respected by all. Skip Vroomberg summed up his personal view of their value to the program this way:

"The Safety guys are just a bunch of sheep running around saying, 'I'm scared!'."

Enough about the Safety people. Plenty of other interesting technical specialists and "experts" adorned the program. There were system/hardware/software design engineers, mechanical engineers, thermal/thermodynamics experts, electrical and electronic engineers, electromagnetic interference experts, computer systems and communications experts, software programmers, simulation developers, test engineers (lab rats), manufacturing people, parts and logistics people, and, barely rounding out the rear fringe of the technical domain for completeness, masters of paperwork, briefing charts, government standards and procedures, rules and regulations, processes and process development.

Individual expertise could be narrowed down to much more specific levels. For example, within the computer systems specialty, there were "Single-Event Upset" experts. Inside the computer's memory, where the programs run, a phenomenon known as a Single Event Upset (SEU) exists whereby a piece of the program code (a "bit", which is stored as either a logical 1 or a logical 0 by a transistor) can be corrupted (reset to the wrong value) by incident radiation. How often this happens is a function of the computer's environment (in this case, the Station's orbit in space) and the shielding around the computer memory. The Space Station's computer systems had to be designed to guard against SEU's as much as was practical and be able to deal with them when they happened. Larry Tosca, the Station's chief software architect, described to us a meeting he had with an SEU expert, revealing without subtlety that building one's reputation on a single, extremely narrow area of expertise may be damaging to one's respect in some circles:

"You know who showed up today? A Popular Largeness Single-Event-Upset toad. He said, 'Every thousand days.'. We said, 'We can live with that.'."

How worried was Larry that it may get back to the gentleman in question that he was referred to in public as a toad? The following exchange provides a hint:

Max Schwantz: "We'll get you a veggie sandwich, Larry."

Larry Tosca: "I hate veggie sandwiches. I like bear fat."

Technical people always question each other's judgement. Sometimes the questioning is based on legitimate technical concerns. Other times the challenge is based on ego. There are also times when questioning (or attacking) another is used as a technique for shifting unwanted attention elsewhere.

Nick Honeydew put in a couple of years as the Manager of the Independent Verification & Validation (IV&V) team at Resistoglide. He was a likeable old salt who lived in a beach house that had its own boat dock and boat. He was divorced, and he chased younger women. His trusty introductory line, which once led to an entertaining exhibition by one of the very friendly locals while we were on a business trip in Houston (as Jose Cabesagrande likes to remind me of from time to time) was, "Hi! Nick Honeydew, Rotarian. Ventura, California."

Nick Honeydew's team's job was to review and criticize other people's designs, based on some industry standards and guidelines. He often lamented, profanely, over how screwed up he thought everything was. For him, the pinnacle of absurdity was achieved when he found out that the toilets on board the Space Station were going to be controlled by computers (known as MDM's):

"We've got MDM's flushing toilets! A PC flushing toilets!!! You like that?!?!"

-Nick Honeydew

The system that had the responsibility for managing the toilets was the Environmental Control & Life Support System (ECLSS). As design engineers assigned to the job of building the EPS, we occasionally liked to see how the other guys were doing with *their* systems (for reassurance purposes at a minimum).

Carl Stevenson: "I understand they had a little problem with their ECLSS system."

Vincent de Cordoba: "Like what?"

Carl Stevenson: "Like making it work."

There were many reasons that explained why the ECLSS engineers, or anyone else, had trouble making their system work. Engineers had to grapple with constantly changing requirements, inconsistent requirements (which led to different components of the same system not working together), infeasible requirements (requirements that are overly difficult, or impossible, to implement), unreliable, or finicky, hardware, crashing [choking, freezing, kaput, "this is an ex-parrot"...] software, faulty test equipment, faulty testers, and daily workarounds (temporary alternatives to technical problems encountered in following the plan). It was a lot to keep up with.

Z-Man Habibi: "Is this [specific flight software requirement] a change?"

Joe Bob Anderson: "No. We've always had this."

Z-Man Habibi: "I think we [the Flight Software team] missed that..."

It's well known that technical talk is not usually crystal clear to most people outside the field. What's less well known is that technical talk is ironically often equally unclear to the experts as well (it's just that experts don't like to admit they are confused in case someone questions their qualifications). Technical conversations can wander all over the place for hours, clouding the air with fancy terminology, imprecise definitions, irrelevant details and plenty of distractions away from the main point. The only thing that breaks the trance and moves the discussion forward is clear communication which makes use of basic terms that are familiar to all.

An example of how clear communication using familiar terms can slam home the point is provided by Joe Bob Anderson, who, on one of many such occasions, was getting nowhere arguing with the customer in technical terms. Oddly enough, I will have to rely on a bit of technical terminology, not wholly different from what I am preaching against, to explain the example.

The discussion centers around a safeguarding control function for software known as Error Detection & Correction (EDAC). EDAC periodically, or upon command, checks the bits (the logical ones and zeros) that are the software program inside a computer's memory to see if they match a specific pattern and corrects (changes) them if they do not. Most software programs can be broken down into an executable component (the part that steps through the logic sequence and operates on the data) and a data component (the specific parameter values that feed the executable). Since *the executable is what performs the EDAC*, EDAC is usually performed on the data space and not the executable.

What started the argument was that the customer wanted our flight software (the software that controls the ISS EPS) to do the EDAC on itself - *including* the executable.

Our objection was that if the software found what it thought were problem bits by doing the EDAC, it would rewrite them, effectively rewriting itself. If the EDAC was ever wrong for some reason, the flight software could be erroneously altered and the control system could be needlessly jeopardized. After what seemed like hours of not getting our point across, Joe Bob Anderson said it this way:

"It's like driving down the freeway at 80 miles an hour and doing brain surgery on yourself."

Clear to all. The customer representative gave up. We successfully moved on to the next subject.

Transposing technical points into common vernacular is an art that is limited only by the artist's ability and imagination. Julius Dusenberg had a natural ability for coming up with some visually-rich, and ultra-memorable analogies. His evaluation of the proposed design for docking the Space Shuttle to the Space Station:

"It's like two blind elephants trying to mate."

On a different occasion, Julius Dusenberg was leading a Station-wide effort to 'channelize' the Space Station's architecture into three separate channels of redundant functionality, each with its own independent power, thermal and control capability. The idea was that if one channel of power/thermal/control experienced a failure, the second and third channels would continue to provide functionality and ensure the safety of the crew and the equipment. If a second channel were to fail, then the third could still provide the vehicle's functionality. The channelized approach should reduce the number of subsystem components per channel to one.

We were explaining to Julius that the thermal control system for each of our photovoltaic power modules was made up of a *single* loop of coolant, which was controlled by *two* pump flow controllers, each of which contained two pumps (making a total of *four* pumps). After he asked us the embarrassing question of why we couldn't find one *good* pump instead of four lousy pumps and we gave him some answer that blamed it on the different failure rates (MTBF) for the different components, he roared out:

"Four pumps!!! It's fucking nuts!!! This guy comes to work with *three* sets of suspenders, *two* jock straps and *one* shoe. Fucking nuts!!!!"

I certainly learned a lot about leadership while working on the Space Station program. Some of what I learned came from a few natural leaders who radiated competence and style. Some came from my own experiences as a first-line manager of a team that, at its peak, was up to thirty engineers. The remainder was generously provided by the unnervingly continual stream of characters who took the reins and so consistently convinced us all how *not* to do it. Lots of people were appointed to leadership positions during my nine years on the project. Most of them were, sooner or later, unappointed.

Except for the earliest years in the life of the Space Station program, my company organized itself based on three principal layers of management - first-line manager, department director, and program manager. First-line managers ran the day-to-day operations of the project and supervised the engineers who did the work. First-line managers were supposed to work strictly within an allocated budget (which changed all the time) and were responsible for making all the deliverables on schedule. They also had to deal with all the personnel issues within their teams, which added healthily to the stress of the job (they got it from above and below). Department directors managed the managers and were responsible for the aggregate budget and set of deliverables. At the top of the organization was the program manager, who was basically responsible for the whole contract. The directors reported to the program manager.

Fortunately for our organization, our program manager for the first eight years, Hannibal Ferguson, was a natural leader (the same cannot be assumed for every program manager who appeared and disappeared throughout all the different organizations that were involved with the Space Station program). Hannibal Ferguson taught me a few practical lessons that applied to life in general.

On the importance of doing one's share for the team and rectifying problems early, Hannibal would encourage one to ask oneself:

"What could I be doing to be contributing to the solution as opposed to watching the problem mature?"

Hannibal liked to put things in simple terms. At a major, three-day vehicle-redesign meeting at NASA Space Station headquarters in Reston, Virginia, Hannibal began to introduce me and another of Resistoglide's young engineers to Brad Northfield (who was the key NASA head honcho presiding over the meetings) this way:

"Things are getting tough, so I brought along some guys who can add and subtract."

Hannibal Ferguson had an outwardly calm but commanding presence when talking with people. He was fully aware of all the work that needed to be done, and he kept the pressure on us to do it. As Maurice (pronounced Morris) Mayfair (with whom the reader will become better acquainted later on in the Culture and Sophistication chapter) put it;

"It's the same thing - Hannibal is the Captain, and the Captain wants to water ski. Keep rowing!"

I liked having Hannibal as our chief. I respected him.

As for some of the other chiefs we had to deal with (from other contractors and the various NASA centers), their ability to lead others was questioned a spectacular number of times. During the same big redesign meeting in Reston, a technical presentation was just about to begin on the vehicle's avionics system (which covered the computer control system architecture, the allocation of functionality to the different computers, and details of the software data management design). Barney Gruffmeister was the meeting's chairman. He asked everyone sitting around the bosses' table to introduce themselves to the rest of the group. When it was MSFC's top representative's turn to speak, he introduced himself and reassured us with the words:

"...and when I say 'avionics', I've expended my knowledge on the subject."

Later, during the same session, Bud Hellcat was presenting a technically detailed chart entitled, 'NOS Simplification' (NOS stood for Network Operating System). The NOS ran the flight core control system network which was a 100 Megabit-per-second, dual-redundant, fiber-optic token ring which operated under the International Standards Organization (ISO) Open System Interconnect (OSI) communication protocol and was being evaluated for simplification. Highly technical stuff. After about twenty minutes of unidirectional word emission from the young presenter to the older, executive audience, the chairman, Barney Gruffmeister, broke in with a question for one of his colleagues from JSC who was seated at the head table:

"Clyde!!! You're the only man in this community that I can talk to. Tell me what he just said."

Barney was just warming up. The next subject addressed failure tolerance and redundancy (how many failures the system could survive and how many duplicate components would be needed). The basic NASA requirement for critical systems was that they be two-failure tolerant, meaning that they had to still be functional after two failures. The most common way of achieving two-failure tolerance was to design the system to basically be three replicas of the exact same thing (triple redundancy). Eventually, after a third failure, whatever components remained alive and well were designed to fail safely in some sort of degraded-performance mode. That means they would execute whatever functions were necessary to preserve the lives of the crew and protect the equipment but would not be able to keep up the original functionality in full. Practical. Basic.

However, when it was being explained to the audience exactly how the avionics system complied with this logic, Barney Gruffmeister became agitated and expressed his disappointment in the proposed design as he didn't understand it:

"With four computers...after three failures...you can't perform two functions ?!?!?!"

Dutch Williams was the senior SC representative at the meeting, and since SC was on contract to build the avionics system, and he was the presenter's supervisor, he snapped back with:

"I'm glad you never learned to count to *five*, Barney".

Dutch Williams was openly fed up and frustrated with the whole arrangement of working for NASA. Maybe he also had some foreboding of what was eventually going to happen to SC. Williams (all the SC people were known to each other and all their friends by their last names) quickly recovered a bit of decorum and tried to explain the matter as straightforwardly as possible:

"Barney, after the third failure, you're going to have to decide whether you want to look at a star or breathe."

Barney still didn't get it. Or he got it, but he didn't like it.

More often than not, the senior guys that were selected to make the decisions that affected the whole program floated along far above the minimum depth of understanding required to effectively make use of their authority. Clyde Cooper, a senior manager out of JSC, and Orville Fitzgerald, another senior manager out of JSC, provide a simple example of the gulf between the power and the knowledge as Clyde asked Orville;

"Do y'all have a 3.1 section of the DMS FSSR [Data Management System Flight System Software Requirements specification]?"

Orville replied without the slightest hesitation;

"Beats the crap out of me."

Now Orville was an intelligent man. He had accomplished some significant things in his career with NASA. He projected leadership qualities, and he was a southern gentleman. He just wasn't fully cognizant of all the details of the situation with which he was put in charge to lead.

Leadership is a tough assignment. Most people can't cut it. The few who can have to stand up to criticism from the people they lead and others around them. They have to consistently perform over the long run. Sometimes expectations run a bit high. My cohort in corporate battlefield strategy, Marcus Electricus, accepted nothing short of perfection from the top. When the NASA Administrator made a rare TV appearance for one of his frequent defenses of the Space Station program in front of Congress, Marcus Electricus attacked him for the sloppy knot in his tie:

"Did you see [the NASA Administrator] on TV?!?! Fuckin' half windsor!!! Looked like shit."

A bit severe, to be sure. Tying a full windsor is not essential for being an effective leader. But knowing the business and the subject matter *is*.

Aside from the technical and management challenges that one would expect to come with building a space station, we had to fight concurrent battles on two other fronts if the project were to have any chance of surviving. The first of these was against an unprecedented monster of world-class bureaucratic politics that thrived on such a huge, geographically-distributed, government project. The second was against all the usual everyday territorial hostility familiar to anyone who has experienced the corporate world.

The politics of the project, vital to motivating Congress to allocate funding in the beginning, almost killed it. On a regular basis. There were simply too many people involved. Things have a higher probability of getting screwed up as the number of people involved increases. The large number of people associated with the Space Station project *guaranteed* that its mission and its top-level requirements were continually re-debated and redefined. This ensured that years (over a decade) would pass before the technical details of the design could escape the blender long enough to solidify into real hardware and software products.

All the worker bees knew there was a big problem. After the first half-dozen major redesigns or so, even people not heralded for their awareness were seriously worried that the project would be cancelled and they would lose their jobs. The old-timers, who preferred that the project last long enough to carry them into the sanctuary of retirement, were worried that all the false starts were going to have the opposite effect and cause the project to be terminated. Lou Alfrito was one such old timer attached to the software team at Resistoglide. Though well past the point where he would want to invest the same amount of time and effort he may have done in the past to try to make things work, Lou at least occasionally managed to mumble and grumble something wise with his own touch of charm:

"We gotta get this thing [the Space Station] done before the Pharaoh dies."

As if the big-picture problems weren't unnerving enough, one had to contend with all the internal power struggles as well. The battle for control began early. When I first arrived at Resistoglide, funding for the Space Station project had just been authorized. I was the second person hired by Resistoglide to work on the Space Station contract (not counting the handful of people who had worked on the winning proposal for the job). As more and more people were hired, and everyone's characteristics, goals, [in]abilities, obsessions and quirks became clearer and clearer, internal contention blossomed.

I formed a solid allegiance early on with two gentlemen I respected and believed in more than anyone else at Resistoglide; Marcus Electricus and The Captain. That trio of The Captain, Marcus Electricus and I formed the foundation upon which our team, the Control System Design Team for the Space Station Electric Power System, was built.

One of the first internal sparring sessions I experienced occurred within my first few months on the project when our management decided to form a 'Senior Design Team' comprised of five or six individuals whose ticket onto this Senior Design Team was either their position within the organization (senior positions from which they were all eventually removed), a Ph.D. in something (repeatedly qualifying its owner to participate - in the softest imaginable sense - in 'important' events in order to impress the customer or visitor who didn't have one) or their age (senior). Although the term 'Senior Design Team' was reassuringly spoken in all the meetings, weeks went by, and these guys didn't produce a thing.

So management formed a new team made up of younger people, junior in rank and not yet bearing the peculiar resistance to progress that, more often than not, encumbers those who manage to stay on the playing field far too long solely by riding on their past achievements. This new team consisted of Marcus Electricus, Archie D'Arc, Celia Chuckleberg and myself. To show how much we respected the feeble thinking that automatically entrusted our 'senior' predecessors with the leadership responsibility for actually producing a design, the four of us called ourselves the '*Sophomore* Design Team'. And, within a couple of weeks, we succeeded in producing the first workable, top-level design of the control system for the Space Station's Electric Power System. Amazing? Not really. Just a capable, small team, wanting to get the job done.

Our design immediately gave everyone else something to shoot at. Every pretender and hibernating-until-someone-else-does-something nay sayer had a go. They attacked the control system architecture, the computer hardware, the control algorithms, the allocation of functions/subfunctions to the distributed processors, the operating modes and software states (constantly confusing the two), and the detailed software requirements. They all failed, one by one, over and over, all those years.

War-time work environments require war-time tactics. If the product was to have a chance of ever being built, I needed to build up an organization made up of highly competent individuals - or, more appropriately, soldiers. The first soldier I recruited was the ambitious, young Jose Cabesagrande. We formed an effective relationship that eluded and vanquished our enemies for years. We were both admirers of the old-world, honor-based method of doing business, and that is how we operated. Jose was my top lieutenant.

One of our most decisive victories came early. Jose, The Captain and I had a showdown with the entire Software Department and its cagey boss at that time, Wiley Method - in front of our customer, NASA LeRC. Following Wiley's lead, the Software Department's strategy was to sit back, do nothing and criticize everything the Control System Design Team (my team) did in trying to define the basic design, gambling that we would fail so they could point the finger at us. They said our control system requirements were not detailed enough to enable them to develop the more-detailed software requirements that they needed and were responsible for generating. When we gave them more details, they said our requirements were too detailed and we were guilty of defining the design beyond the boundary of our authority, trespassing on their turf.

This was a shameful situation that had to change. My team had to be given the full authority to define all the software requirements because Wiley's department didn't have what it takes. The customer backed us 100% as we wrenched total control of the software requirements away from Wiley Method's impotent-in-doing-real-work-yet-tireless-in-trying-to-keep-others-from-doing-so
organization. My team blasted ahead and defined the software requirements at a detailed-enough level to allow the flight software for the station's electric power system to be written.

When the pleasantly-surprised customer endorsed our requirements at the first of a series of formal reviews, the Software Department suddenly had a lot of catch-up work to do. Soon thereafter, the Software Department was dissolved and absorbed by another department under another director as part of a major reorganization. Wiley Method was given an advisory position and managed to remain involved in software development from a safe distance (safe enough for us and safe enough for him).

Over time, Wiley and I realized that, in spite of all the battles we had fought against each other, we actually had something in common - an unlikely (certainly in this industry, and in society in general) appreciation for literature and the correct use of the English language. It would be unfair of me not to acknowledge that, as our control system matured and was well on its way to being built and working, Wiley made up for his earlier behavior to some extent by making a number of beneficial contributions to the common goal.

There were still plenty of other kinds of problems still left to be dealt with. One of these was my team's having to depend on shared computer resources that were controlled by another organization. It taught us the lesson of minimizing, if not completely eliminating, one's dependence on others in order to get the job done. This is one of the most important lessons in the engineering business. The computer network we depended on to develop and run our simulation of the electric power system was administered by two system managers who reported to another manager. They regularly did things that caused our simulation to crash (stop working and hang up) without apologizing or showing the slightest concern.

Marcus Electricus resorted to having to discretely modify the parameters of the operating system to increase the levels of priority and protection for our simulation. The system managers would eventually discover what he did and reset the parameters to something worse than before. Their behavior was consistent with the theory that system managers like these often suffer from a superiority complex within their very narrow field of expertise and don't like being challenged by people outside their field who are smarter than them at what they're supposed to be smartest at doing.

After a nightmare battle with our own purchasing process [I challenge you to read Appendix P *all the way to its end!*], we finally acquired a much more powerful, stand-alone workstation and disengaged ourselves from the network and its two tyrants. We never again had a problem with crashing computers because of the network. In the long run, and after we removed our dependency on them, these two people who had caused us so much bother both wound up leaving the company under shady circumstances...to no one's despair.

Besides big, specific battles like the software requirements and the computer network, there was an assortment of ne'er-do-wells who, either intentionally, or a la Inspector Clouseau, created diabolical problems for us whenever possible and threatened our likelihood for getting the job done. Fortunately, they were no match for the spirit and confidence of an army that had generals like Marcus Electricus, who's motivation came from deep within and whose determination and ability did not depend on others. As he said:

"Let's succeed, despite not having a worthy opponent."

A lot of 'old guys' wound up working on the Space Station project, which was mostly made up of people in their thirties and forties. Some rolled in off other, dying projects at the start. Others were called out of retirement to try to straighten things out. Some of them converted their experiences of the past into something useful for the present. Others were just hanging on dearly until they had enough points to retire.

The most revered (by the handful of young and dedicated engineers, at least) of the valuable-category old guys was Julius Dusenberg. The fact that so many of the old guys in power were afraid of Julius only endeared him further with the bright young engineers who were fortunate enough to have been selected to work with him. Julius was our Napoleon, our Alexander the Great. We would have followed him anywhere because he was larger than life, believable, credible, unstoppable.

Julius' extensive experience in the business was almost always helpful to us. It was helpful because (1) the statements he made were - though probably painful for the people at whose expense the lessons were learned - accurate, (2) he knew when to make them, and (3) he transformed complicated, technical subjects into the intuitive and the obvious.

One time, in a design review meeting, while someone managed to successfully digress from the main issue on the table by expressing disgruntlement over the fact that the software was not perfect the first time, Julius quickly got the meeting back on track:

"The rule on software is - you fix it. That's why it's *soft*ware."

On another occasion, the argument was whether or not commercial, off-the-shelf equipment (as opposed to custom-made for NASA) should be used as part of the actual flight design, which would violate the NASA tradition of building almost everything from scratch. The concern was that the custom stuff did not look like it was going to be built on time to meet the flight schedule. The proponents of Wasteful Promotion of Oneself and One's Organization (building, and charging for, everything themselves) questioned the fidelity of the commercial products. Julius killed that argument this way:

"The commercial equipment in our lab [the equipment used to *test* the flight hardware and software] works better than the stuff we're checking out. Otherwise, we wouldn't use it."

Although Julius' involvement wasn't enough to make a difference on that day (commercial, off-the-shelf products were not incorporated as part of the mission-critical flight system), it did make a difference concerning many other issues in the long run. Julius made us think.

To make a difference, 'lessons learned' should effect improvement and not just be a convenient little phrase to excuse repeated mistakes. In a business where people's lives are on the line, it's never too late to do the job right. Designs should be simple, elegant. Engineers should build their systems to detect, pinpoint and contain failures safely, no matter how improbable a particular failure may be. "Yeah, I know, one chance in a million based on the studies - but what is your system going to do when that failure *does* occur? Why don't you design the system so you don't care what the odds are?", Julius would ask us. And building upon a solid design foundation, flight hardware and software components should be thoroughly tested; first individually and then again as an integrated system. Uncommon common sense. Insightful thinking requires intelligent supporters to appreciate the concepts and act them out without prejudice. I am grateful to have worked with a few such people across the program, and I know that at least some of their precious lessons from experience were not wasted.

3.1.2.26 *Sound Advice*

The difference between sound advice - advice one can actually count on - and waves of babble that flow from the well-worn mouths of intrusive busybodies depends on who is giving the advice and how often they give it. Smart people who don't often give advice are usually a good source for sound advice.

In the case of my good friend from SGT, Skip Vroomberg, deservedly well-respected but prone to (more accurately, unable to deviate from) high-speed, animated, endurance yakity yak yak, the advice he received from Floyd Crawdad following the latest of a long series of detailed technical presentations that inevitably spun out of control was priceless:

"A friendly hint - you talk too much."

Floyd clearly qualified as a good source for advice. He was smart, and he didn't usually give advice. He liked Skip, and he knew how much hard work went into his presentations. Floyd meant every word he said. This was truly a helpful hint. And the hint came from a friend. Skip talked too much. That's it. Simple. Clear.

Simplicity and clarity are two key ingredients the advice giver must project if the advice is to be remembered so it can make itself useful. Most people have been through experiences that have demonstrated to them the hard way that one failure can quickly take away what required a lot more successes to build up. That is a difficult imbalance to accept intuitively. So unless we are occasionally reminded of that danger in an easy-to-remember, tailored-for-the-listener piece of sound advice, we will have to keep on learning that lesson again and again. Dutch Williams got it across to Carving Bear this way:

"It takes a thousand 'attaboys' just to wipe out one 'aw, shit'. Just remember that, Carving."

It's a tough world. One has to fight to get somewhere (to build a reputation, to deserve recognition), and one has to fight to stay there (to maintain that reputation and stay worthy of that recognition). It was no different on the Space Station project. Getting, and holding on to, a piece of the project meant money and jobs. Not getting, or losing, a piece of it meant layoffs. There were many decisive meetings over the years at which a big piece of, or maybe all, the business was on the line. There was one such meeting in Reston, where Resistoglide's boss for Space Station, Hannibal Ferguson, made sure I understood the gravity of the situation:

"When the music stops, grab a chair."

Simple. Clear.

3.2.1.27 *Culture & Sophistication*

It was always a refreshing treat for me to encounter, and converse with, all-around-well-educated, renaissance-like individuals who worked on the Space Station project because, understandably, the majority of people in that line of work need not extend themselves beyond their expertise in technical matters or the shifty ways of long-term-self-supporting 'management' or process-analysis paralysis.

Four people I worked with who retained their individual sense of worldly depth in spite of the highly regulated culture of the aerospace business were Marcus Electricus, Z-Man Habibi, Greta Beren-Auslese and Maurice Mayfair.

Marcus Electricus knew so many things. He had read a lot of books while he was growing up in Pittsburgh. It impressed me that he knew so much about world history and geography without having traveled extensively. We enjoyed stimulating conversations about the Romans, the Gauls, the American Civil War, the French Revolution, Churchill, World Wars I and II, Ghengis Khan, Napoleon, Alexander the Great, Ben Franklin, Edison, Van Gogh, Hemingway... the North American freshwater turtle (Marcus even defined for us the word 'terrapin' as we puzzled over the title of that most excellent Grateful Dead album).

They way I saw it, Marcus was the program's only true master in the area of electric power systems. There were a few smart-guy specialists here and there, and plenty of pretenders, but Marcus really lived, breathed and sparkled with what they only flirted with - which magnified my amazement at how much else he knew. It was always a delight to learn something new from him:

"Actually, polo is a medieval game. The winners - they played with the head of the loser."

One time, Marcus and I were reviewing one of our many strategic battle plans at work (inevitably traceable back to Sun Tzu's "The Art of War"), when the famous phrase, "Veni, Vidi, Vici" came up. Embarrassing for us both, neither of us could be sure who had originally said it.

We were given the answer by Greta Beren-Auslese, a perpetually energetic Berliner, who took it upon herself to find out. The next day, she told us the statement was made by Gaius Julius Caesar when he defeated Pharnaces, son of Mithridates, at Zela in Asia Minor in 47 B.C.. That took care of that.

Greta was a contemporary aristocrat. Her society was the older, scholarly wine-drinking set who lived in the Hollywood Hills. She drove a Mercedes diesel station wagon (with 250,000 miles on its odometer, she loved to tell me, proudly) and once flew in an F-15 fighter plane (which was less of a big deal to her than it would have been to me). Every Christmas, she used to give me a present of special chocolates that were filled with top-shelf liqueurs and sold without the proper authorization by some shopkeeper in Beverly Hills.

In matters of dress, social protocol, automobiles, and choice of cocktail, Z-Man Habibi defined the upper limits for the Space Station project. Almost always in a smart, double-breasted jacket with tie and stylish Italian shoes (Ferragamo, no less!), he was a classic gentleman. He was always polite and courteous, which was consistent with his culture and upbringing. He drove a black BMW for the first few years I knew him, then a black Lexus. He told me he worked hard and owed it to himself (actually, he owed the bank). This was an attractive, and not unfamiliar, sentiment to me as I used to drive a black Porsche before more conservative sentiments regained control and I sold it for the downpayment on my home.

The characteristic I found most distinctive within Z-Man's portfolio of sophistication had to be his favorite drink, Courvoisier cognac. The two most notable points here are (1) he genuinely liked the drink (he wasn't just putting on a show to impress people), and (2) there were a lot of funny looks on the faces of the waiters and bartenders in Texas whenever he tried to order it.

The fourth person who could certainly be counted on to impress upon others his familiarity with the finer things in life was Maurice Mayfair. Maurice came to LA from London in the sixties. He opted for working in America and enjoying a California lifestyle (complete with 1965 Mustang convertible) but held on to a few, timeless cultural idiosyncrasies that were distinctly British. These included his permanent English accent, Saville Row mohair suits, and a taste for - and ability to locate in LA – 'proper' beer like Guinness on tap and Mackeson's XXXX.

Maurice and his wife were active members of the British Association of Film and Television Arts and the British American Chamber of Commerce. They often went to social affairs put on for visiting British royalty, MP's and other VIP's. At one such 'do', Maurice recalled how he was approached by a flirtatious woman and how he deftly - though not without some sense of missed opportunity, I'm sure - avoided big trouble:

Woman at British social function: "Who are you?"

Maurice Mayfair: "I'm James Bond."

Woman: "Oooh! You have quite a reputation, Mr. Bond. Are you up to it?!"

Maurice Mayfair: "Meet my wife, 008."

Maurice was always telling me stories about his friends who made lots of money and drove Rolls Royces. Thanks to one of those friends, Maurice once got us tickets to an Arsenal football match while we were both in England one Christmas holiday - not out in the stands in the rain "with the hoi polloi" (as he took great delight in pointing out repeatedly), but in a heated executive box, complete with personal waitress service and a television for replays. Quintessential Mayfair.

Maurice also used to go to cricket matches in the San Fernando Valley to socialize. Of course, the only civilized way to watch a game of cricket in California was to sit on a lawn chair, in the shade, sipping champagne. When one admiring young greenhorn anglophile once asked him how one gains entrance into such an obviously savvy group, Maurice replied:

"A decent bottle of champagne."

Maurice was ever ready to make known his opinion of what was proper (executive box) and what was lesser (standing in the cold English rain) on any eligible issue, including shoes. Lightweight, Italian moccasins were an appealing choice of footwear during the hot LA summers. However, even in such heat, Maurice would never accept them as *proper* business shoes for gentlemen. He always wore the more classically styled business shoes one would be more likely to see in The City (London), and he once teased me for wearing the lighter moccasins by saying, in the presence of one or two others:

"Those are nice. Do they make them for *men*?!"

I don't wear that kind of shoe anymore. I don't really know if it's because Maurice gave me a complex or if I'm just getting older and I want sensible shoes that will last me longer.

Marcus Electricus, Z-Man Habibi, Greta Beren-Auslese and Maurice Mayfair brought a rare touch of cultural magic to the Space Station project. They could make any project fun to work on. They clearly were not suppressed by the aerospace industry and its inherent limitations on style and character. They each came from somewhere else, with a strong sense of personal identity that wasn't about to be diluted or subdued by this project or any other, no matter how many decades went by.

I realize now, looking back at all the chapters and all the quotes, that most of my fondest recollections from working on the Space Station project came from the earlier years when it was known as Space Station Freedom and when four different NASA centers managed three prime contractors. When the project underwent its most dramatic management restructure, and management control was centralized under JSC with Popular Largeness as the prime contractor, things changed.

The way Popular Largeness operated was to create special-purpose teams for everything, generate process charts with lots of bubbles and arrows pointing everywhere, and measure everything with metrics (number of this or that plotted out in graphs for reporting to management). When more and more teams are created, more and more communication and coordination is simultaneously needed between them. Reporting metrics up the line to management winds up taking more time than building the thing the contract says to build (this is *not* an exaggeration).

I specifically recall one particular weekly metrics report that was due to a senior NASA person in Houston every Saturday. To be ready by Saturday, the scheduling people at each of the contractors collected inputs from the people closest to the products (like my team) on Tuesday. That same day, as well as the next, we used to receive phone calls from our counterparts at Popular Largeness asking for the same information and checking to see what we were going to say. Thursday required a three-hour telecon for some Popular Largeness middle manager to check things out before the Friday presentation to the Popular Largeness program manager which took place before the data were shown to the big boss the next day. All in all, hundreds of people running around, spending obscene amounts of time making charts and filtering data instead of working on the problems.

During one of an endless series of weekly telecons hosted by the subcontractor responsible for providing most of the computer hardware and software to all the flight system developers across the program, a discussion was taking place regarding some long-standing problems with the flight software compiler. The compiler was essential to building the flight software. Mitch Stevens, the responsible engineer, was increasingly being dragged away from his work to one meeting after another to deliver the latest status of the compiler problems:

Mitch Stevens: "That [one particular] problem is fixed, but other problems are occuring downstream."

[the metric-driven contract manager]: "How are you accounting for the additional problems?"

Mitch Stevens: "I'm *not* accounting for them. I'm just *working* them."

I noticed, repeatedly, that pointing out the absurdity of spending more time and resources on reporting the status of problems than actually solving them was less often met with laughter than with acquiescent grumbling (even from the younger engineers). The metrics were so extreme, they slowly sucked the life out of those who had to provide them. Nobody was enjoying themselves any more.

Suspicions that maybe my time on the project was coming to an end were bolstered by an incident that centered around the metrics that were supposed to quantify the status of our testing of the EPS software. Elroy Yeager, a Floridian with a pilot's license, a peeling black Corvette and premature gray hair to match, was our team's lead engineer for software testing. He had to produce these data daily for the head of the department. The department head was not a nice man. "Insecure" and "abusive" topped the opinion polls. He bullied the people who worked for him, and the able ones left.

Elroy tracked the number of requirements tested, the number untested, the number passed and the number failed. The Flight Software team (Z-Man's team) was represented by Jose Cabesagrande, who had moved to that team from mine to lead the development effort for the Photovoltaic Controller software. Jose had to explain every failure. To avoid as much verbal abuse and derision as possible from 'Ivan the Intolerable', Jose did his best to twist and coax the numbers to a more favorable representation of the state of the software.

If the numbers overrated the quality of the software, and Elroy performed a more detailed test later on that showed the software to contain more problems than has been reported, Elroy would get screwed for falsifying data. One day, Elroy told me he was extremely annoyed because he had spent his whole day preparing 'countermetrics'. This, pathetically, is what these two well-respected engineers had been reduced to.

The Space Station project had succumbed to management-itis. 'Earned value', cost and schedule variances (how much under/over budget, how far ahead of/behind schedule), recovery plans, 'estimates at completion' (budget predictions out to the year 2002), budget 'reconciliations' (an inoffensive term for reductions), contractual change papers, and detailed schedules dominated most people's time at work.

155

Technical activity was slowly being suffocated by the accountants and administrators.

To make matters worse for the dwindling number of technical engineers (sadly, not an oxymoron here) who had not yet bailed out from the project, we were subjected to a torrent of company 'initiatives' that couldn't have come at a worse time. These bizarre exercises, flowed down from the top because some too-readily-believed study or consultant said they are what the company needs in order to be 'world class' (i.e., to keep being awarded contracts), included:

- Endless, and mostly mandatory, mass training classes (with revealing names like 'Diversity in the Workforce', 'Managing Compliance', 'Quality Function Deployment', 'Ergonomic Injury Prevention for the Office', 'Hazardous Material Communications', 'Ethics Refresher' [this course worried me the most: *"Bob awards a subcontract to his brother-in-law. Do you see any problem with that?"*], 'Time Management', 'Image and Self Projection', 'Releasing Human Potential 1/2/3', 'Building Trust and Credibility', 'Safety Training', 'Leadership', 'Total Quality Management', 'Continuous Process Improvement', 'Truth in Negotiations', 'Won't Fail Practices', 'Violence in the Workforce'...)

- Housekeeping inspections (which rated offices and labs as 'green', 'yellow' and 'red' - 'green' being the goal, attainable only by getting rid of everything from the tops of desks, posting nothing without a frame on the walls, erasing all markings from marker boards, and lining up computer mouse pads neatly)

- Ever-more-complicated annual changes to the employee performance review process (which got to the point where numerous surveys - containing over a hundred and fifty questions each - had to be filled out and sent to a professional survey processing company, numerous meetings had to be held with the employee and their manager, and numerous months went by before the same 3% average raise was handed out just like before

- A company desire to attain a Software Engineering Institute Level 3 rating by the end of the year in order to impress slow-thinking, potential customers enough to give Resistoglide new work (you don't want to know to what extent hundreds of basic, on-the-job procedures have to be written down and continually revised for this baby!)

- ...and the magically-self-imposing, extremely fashionable (though thoroughly extraneous) ISO 9001 certification (which, among other foolishness, requires people to stamp "For Information Only" on everything not directly used in the production path - like office documents and furniture - to guard against anyone accidentally coding to the 'Releasing Human Potential 1/2/3' course materials instead of the latest requirements document)

Farcical.

But these were the signs of the new order. I could not deny the new reality. I had had enough, and I left the project to return to commercial industry. There was a ton of stuff to catch up on, having been insulated for so long from the advancements in the rapidly moving world of commercial technology.

Difficult as it was for me to accept at first, I understood why all my prospective employers in the commercial industry needed to be convinced that I was really OK even though I had worked in the aerospace industry for so many years. Since the aerospace industry generally complies with the 80-20 Rule (80% of the people do 20% of the work, leaving 20% of the people to do 80% of the work), one is more likely to be part of the substandard 80 than the outstanding 20. As one prospective employer in the commercial industry told me, it's more cost effective for them to simply play the odds and steer clear of aerospace people altogether.

3.1.2.29 Epilogue

My big space adventure is over now, but the International Space Station that I helped design is finally, amazingly, starting to materialize in space. On November 20, 1998, the first element of the ISS was successfully launched into orbit from Russia. The second element went up in the Space Shuttle Endeavor two weeks later, on December 4th.

It will be a proud day for me when they activate the EPS control system in orbit. I also know that each of my capable colleagues across the program (past and present) will fulfill their dreams when they finally get to see the successful outcome of their hard work.

I stepped into the aerospace world and joined this great project full of romantic notions of space exploration and NASA glory. Alternating feelings of gratitude and disbelief quivered inside me because people were putting their trust in *me* to design and test such a critical part of the International Space Station.

As time passed, I learned from the inside how NASA and the space industry operated. I learned 'acronym-speak' and generated my own acronyms to add to the official list. I learned all the program's processes; what they were designed to achieve, what they were designed to prevent, how they sometimes prevented what they were designed to achieve, and how to go around them to make sure that the important stuff got done.

I learned who's who; heroes from the past and new hot shots. I experienced frustration as the fate of the project was debated yearly and continual rescoping and redesigning kept killing any hard-won progress. I saw organizations and their proponents come and go. I saw good people leave and incompetents promoted (usually holding on to their new positions long enough to do some damage but not long enough to sink the ship). I also saw new people recognized for work that was done by their predecessors (a phenomenon certainly not unique to this project or this industry).

I worked with people who put in a strenuous amount of overtime (which was costly to their health and their marriages) while others watched the clock and played the stock market. I once signed Marcus Electricus' time card after he had logged <u>one hundred and one hours in a single week</u> to install and debug his simulation at the customer site in Houston.

I persevered with the project long enough to see the real product escape the paper, overcoming the subversion of the detractors and the effortless repression by the bureaucracy. There were too many people involved with the Space Station project - way too many. I know that politics make the job tough, but if it were my baby to command, I would have kept the team small and only hired the capable people. Maybe next time.

In the end, I'm content ('relieved' might be more accurate). It sure would have been one Texas-size heartbreaker if all that effort had been for naught. A part of me went into the International Space Station. That's what I wanted. It could certainly have been a lot easier, but that, as the adventurers all say, would certainly have been a lot less satisfying.

The way I see it, Captain, the real marvel of the International Space Station is not so much the vehicle itself or its promise of discovery but the gratifying triumph of wit and spirit over the long-refined shortcomings of human nature.

As I cleaned out my office and sorted through all my old stuff, Marcus Electricus kept me company:

Vincent de Cordoba: "Want to read some neural network articles?"

Marcus Electricus: "No, not particularly. I've had it with everything."

)hn Dundee indicate that
ust now be written to the
justifying the capital
office writes the AR.

Appendix P

*This is a dated log of the procure*ome key software to run
computer and supporting hardwa
requested for testing the EPS
Software. **This is an actual accou** Meeting held with John
cts department], Vincent

2 contract with HIP, Inc.

Mar 24, 1993 - 36Q's (procuren
VAX 4000/90, Software Devel
TCP/IP [standard, international r
protocol] Software, and Mil-St
communication protocol] Commu
John Prey to begin the procuremer

Mar 25, 1993 - John Prey gives
(John Dundee is the assigned 'ind
John Prey and John Dundee indic
that the 36Q's and the baseline
system are different.   They su*ment process for a VAX*
[internal letter] stating it's OK.   *ure and software that we*
S Control System and
Mar 26, 1993 - The IL showing*unt.*
the 36Q's and the baseline flight c
is written from Archie D'Arc to
Copies are given to John Prey and ment request forms) for

Apr 01, 1993 - John Prey and Jo lopment Tool License,
an 'Acquisition Request' (AR) mu network communication
company president, Big John, td-1553 [flight system
expense. John Prey says that his o unication Cards given to
nt process.

Apr 05, 1993 - 36Q for software
[small company that will write so 3 36Q's to John Dundee
on the VAX] given to John Prey. dustrial engineer'). Both
icate a problem exists in
Apr 15, 1993 - Confusion exists. flight computer control
Prey, Jane Jeans [from the Contra ggest we write an IL

162   3 the difference between
computer control system
to Vincent de Cordoba.
d John Dundee

de Cordoba, Manager of Control System Design Team (CSD), Archie D'Arc [control system and software test lead engineer], and Art Chartwell [our department head]. John Prey explains the AR process again and states that the AR has not been started. Jane Jeans feels that none of the equipment being requested should be designated as part of the existing Space Station contract. John Prey gives an AR form to Vincent de Cordoba and Archie D'Arc to fill in. This is the first time we, CSD, find out that we must complete the AR form.

Apr 20, 1993 - AR completed by CSD for John Prey. He comes back with some modifications and says he'll do the lease-versus-buy trade study portion of the AR. CSD gives back the AR with the changes incorporated. John Prey explains the capital versus contract procedures for us. He will look over the AR, type it up, and assign an 'industrial engineer' to follow it through the system. He explains the signature cycle and tells us that he will put it through the procurement cycle in parallel with the signature cycle to speed things up. He also says he'll resolve the TCP/IP capital (Resistoglide pays) versus contract (NASA pays as part of Space Station contract) issue.

Apr 27, 1993 - Art Chartwell has meeting with Finance Department Director, Al Chimes, to discuss the capital versus contract issues. Al Chimes agrees that we should just follow the quickest path. Archie D'Arc leaves message with John Prey to find out status. No response (he's in some sort of training class).

Apr 30, 1993 - CSD calls John Prey. Nothing to report.

May 03, 1993 - CSD told by John Prey that the 36Q's/AR were assigned to John O'Brian. CSD contacts him to find out status. He will contact us later today.

May 04, 1993 - CSD calls John O'Brian again. He says the AR was rejected at the first step in the signature cycle because it did not have the lease-versus-buy option completed. Still more confusion about the VAX 4000/90 and the capital versus contract issue. John O'Brian states that CSD should do the lease-versus-buy trade study to help speed up the process (!). John O'Brian still needs more time to become familiar with the 36Q's because he's "only had them a week and a half". He says the 36Q's can't go to the procurement people until the signature cycle is completed because they might not be approved. The HIP 36Q is given to Joe Monk in Budgets/Planning for new contract numbers and to start the 36Q process all over again as contract. CSD meets with Art Chartwell to lament about the extremely slow procurement progress.

May 05, 1993 - Art Chartwell talked last night with Al Chimes and John Stuttgart [Resistoglide Deputy Space Station Program Manager]. They decided that all purchases for control system and software testing for Space Station will be made under contract. Jane Jeans will be assigned to facilitate procurement. CSD will write a justification letter using a previous purchase of some test equipment as a guideline. Jane will then get approval from Tim Smoothly, the on-site NASA representative. Concurrently, we must rewrite our part of a parallel proposal activity to be consistent with all that has transpired (putting everything on contract and incorporating the present equipment list). Joe Monk has been informed of the decision to go all contract. He needs to make new contract numbers for all the purchases. New 36Q's will be issued. Jane Jeans is aware of the situation. She states that our points of contact will be Joe Monk and John Starter [Materials Services representative]. She states that a new form must accompany the 36Q's called an EIEIO (engineering equipment order) and to ask John

Starter how to fill it out. She states that she won't see the 36Q's in her hands for another two months (personal note - try to find out why).

May 07, 1993 - Joe Monk is still working the contract numbers and has to fill out a Budget Change Request (BCR) in order to get the money. Several calls were made to John Starter with no response. In the meantime, we are working on the wording for the justification portion of the EIEIO. Joe Monk gave a heads-up to several people including Jane Beene of Accounting and John Mealy of Property Administration. Maggie Dallas [CSD] talked to John Toro of Material Services. John Toro will be helping John Starter push things through the system. John Toro will type up the EIEIO when he gets it from us. We need Jane Jeans' approval first. John Toro says the 36Q's must go through Property Administration (at both the Resistoglide and NASA Property organizations), then through the signature cycle and then through Purchasing. Archie D'Arc believes the process goes something like this:

1) Art Chartwell signs, Hannibal Ferguson signs
2) Paperwork given to Material Services (John Toro and John Starter)
3) Paperwork goes to Property Administration (John Mealy) to check that similar property does not exist here or at NASA
4) Paperwork goes to Jane Jeans (Contracts)
5) Jane Jeans gives paperwork to Tim Smoothly (NASA rep) for approval
6) Paperwork goes out to Purchasing department

Jane Jeans approves what we wrote for the EIEIO. She will pass it on to John Mealy for his approval. Once they have both approved it, we will take it and the 36Q's over to John Toro. Jane Beene of Accounting approves the new account numbers Joe Monk came up with.

[Absurd and annoying already, no? Keep reading...]

May 10, 1993 - Vincent de Cordoba and Maggie Dallas got the signatures from Art Chartwell and Hannibal Ferguson. Now waiting for Jane Jeans' approval.

May 11, 1993 - Jane Jeans says we are to wait until we hear from her before we submit the 36Q's to Material Services.

May 12, 1993 - Jane Jeans says she needs to get her manager's approval first. She has to justify the expense to her manager.

May 17, 1993 - Jane Jeans calls Vincent de Cordoba. She says to go ahead and give the 36Q's and EIEIO's to John Starter, Material Services. Jane Jeans is still trying to classify the equipment as contract. She will send a Fax to Vincent de Cordoba to review and send back with an OK. If she is unable to go ahead with the contract classification, she will pursue the 'plant equipment' approach, which is capital equipment purchased for a contract.

May 18, 1993 - Five 36Q's are given to John Starter this morning. John Starter gives 36Q's to John Toro. John Toro will be writing EIEIO's. John Starter needs additional information regarding price breakdown for VAX 4000/90 so Property Administration can tag each item. Archie D'Arc works on the breakdown and provides the information to John Toro.

May 20, 1993 - John Toro requests that the flysheet which accompanies the VAX 4000/90 36Q be reformatted. Archie D'Arc reformats the flysheet and returns it to John Toro.

May 24, 1993 - John Toro tells us that the 36Q's are still in the cycle and everything is looking good.

Jun 02, 1993 - John Toro tells us that everything got signed off except the 36Q for the VAX 4000/90. That 36Q was rejected by Property Administration. They need more information regarding the justification for why the VAX should be classified as Special Test Equipment (STE).

Jun 03, 1993 - Archie D'Arc and Vincent de Cordoba go and talk to John Toro to find out the details of the rejection. We learn that there is a Federal Acquisition Regulation (FAR) governing STE. We also learn that a woman from the on-site government regulation office, Jane Sport, can write a letter to Resistoglide saying that the purchase is OK as STE. A letter such as this should speed the processing of this 36Q through Property Administration.

Jun 08, 1993 - Archie D'Arc and Vincent de Cordoba talk to Marty Wagner and Earl Marlborough of LeRC about the status of the 36Q's. We urge them to get in touch with Jane Sport and inform her that the equipment should be purchased as STE.

Jun 10, 1993 - Marty Wagner notifies Jane Sport that LeRC approved the equipment as STE. After clearing up some confusion between our equipment and a similar purchase, Jane Sport agreed that the equipment should be STE.

Jun 13, 1993 - Archie D'Arc calls John Toro about the status of the 36Q's. Property Administration still will not sign them. Archie D'Arc and Vincent de Cordoba talk with Jane Jeans. She says she will try to get the 36Q's out of Property Administration for us. She also tells us that she could get Jane Sport to write the approval letter for us. However, Jane Jeans must have the 36Q's before Jane Sport can write the letter. Jane Sport's letter cannot get the 36Q's out of Property Administration right now.

Jun 16, 1993 - CSD talks with John Mealy. He claims not to understand why the VAX 4000/90 should be classified as STE. Archie D'Arc described to him the nature of our testing and the relationship to the test equipment. John Mealy requested that this information be written down in an IL so he could sign off on the 36Q's.

Jun 17, 1993 - Archie D'Arc writes the IL describing the nature of the testing and the special equipment needed. The IL specifically details the planned modifications to the VAX 4000/90 which will make it a non-standard VAX. A schematic of the entire testbed facility and a copy of the original STE justification are attached. The package is delivered to both John Mealy and John Toro.

Jun 21, 1993 - Archie D'Arc talks with John Toro. The IL seems to have helped a bit. John Mealy has asked John Toro to do a few minor things (??) before he will sign the 36Q. The signature should materialize by the end of the day.

Jun 22, 1993 - Archie D'Arc talks with John Toro again. John Mealy has asked John Toro to do a couple more minor things (???) and then he will sign. Vincent de Cordoba calls John Mealy to tell him that it is urgent that the 36Q gets signed today. John Mealy talks to one of his employees who is "dealing with it" and says it should be signed today. NASA LeRC is getting very frustrated with Resistoglide regarding this purchase. They feel like they have done all that they can from their end, and they don't understand why Resistoglide cannot get these 36Q's out. LeRC has reminded Resistoglide that the delivery and integration of this equipment is scheduled to begin July 1st, 1993. LeRC does not want the schedule to slip.

Jun 23, 1993 - Miraculously, John Toro informs us that the issue of purchasing the VAX 4000/90 as STE has been resolved. John Mealy has now assigned the 36Q to John Door. John Door will deliver the 36Q to [a different Resistoglide facility], get it back, and have a letter typed to Jane Jeans. He will then deliver the 36Q to Jane Jeans. John Toro said that this process should take three to four days.

Jul 01, 1993 - Vincent de Cordoba continues to get pounded on regarding the extremely slow progress. Vincent de Cordoba informs John Toro of this. Vincent also tells John Toro that Art Chartwell wants a flow chart of all the remaining steps that need to be taken at Resistoglide before the 36Q's go out to NASA LeRC. John Toro says that he will track down the 36Q's to see where they are (!) and let Vincent de Cordoba know. John Toro later leaves a message for Vincent saying that the paperwork has been sent to Facilities and Plant Operations "for screening".

Jul 02, 1993 - John Toro calls Vincent de Cordoba and leaves a message saying that the 36Q's are at Facilities and Plant Operations and that there is an individual who is "working on them". John Toro expects to hand carry them back by Tuesday, July 6th. Vincent de Cordoba calls John Toro. John Toro says that John Newman, Facilities and Plant Operations, has the paperwork. John Toro will get it personally on the 6th. After that, the following must happen to the 36Q's:

1) John Door, Property Administration, types up an IL
2) Jane Jeans, Contracts, has up to 30 days to type up an IL
3) Tim Smoothly, NASA Rep, signs

4) Paperwork goes back to Contracts
5) Paperwork goes back to Property Administration
6) Paperwork goes back to Material Services
7) Paperwork goes to Purchasing (unknown how long the actual purchasing will take)

John Toro says he has drafted the flowchart Art Chartwell wanted.

Jul 06, 1993 - Vincent de Cordoba talks with John Toro. The 36Q's are still with Facilities and Plant Operations. John Newman is "getting things typed up" and needs to get his director's signature. He should have that by the end of the day or first thing tomorrow.

Jul 07, 1993 - Archie D'Arc talks with John Toro. John Toro says that John Newman is still waiting for his director's signature. Archie D'Arc and Vincent de Cordoba talk with John Newman. He says that his director just signed "the 1518" and everything should be ready. John Door says that he could send them via internal company mail to us but he cannot personally deliver them from his facility. Archie D'Arc talks with John Toro again. He says his management will not let him drive over there to pick up the package. So Vincent de Cordoba sends the youngest member of the CSD team, Sivonikus Juris, to pick up the package and hand deliver it to John Toro.

Jul 08, 1993 - John Toro calls Archie D'Arc to update the status of the 36Q's. John Toro has given the 36Q's to John Door. John Door is treating this as a priority job (!). He should be finished with processing the paperwork and taking it over to Contracts today.

Jul 09, 1993 - John Toro calls to inform us that the 36Q's are now with Contracts. They are expected to be there for about two weeks.

Jul 13, 1993 - Archie D'Arc calls Jane Jeans for a status update on the 36Q's. They are presently with Al Chimes awaiting his signature. After Al Chimes signs them, they will go to Tim Smoothly for signature and then be Faxed to NASA LeRC. She expects that they will be Faxed to LeRC in a couple of days.

Jul 15, 1993 - Archie D'Arc runs into Tim Smoothly. Tim Smoothly says he has signed the 36Q's. Archie D'Arc leaves a message with Marty Wagner relaying this information and asking him to confirm that LeRC has received the 36Q's.

Jul 19, 1993 - Archie D'Arc calls Marty Wagner to confirm that the 36Q's made it to LeRC. Marty Wagner says that he left a message with Jim Stone (the person at LeRC who should receive them) to call as soon as he gets the Fax. Marty Wagner has not yet heard anything back. Archie D'Arc talks with Jane Jeans. She says the 36Q's were shipped to LeRC FedEx on Tuesday or Wednesday of last week.

Jul 28, 1993 - Marty Wagner says that LeRC has approved the purchase of the equipment. Archie D'Arc talks with Jane Jeans to confirm this. Jane says that she has received verbal approval but has not yet received anything in writing. When she does, the package will go back to Property Administration, who will then release the package to Purchasing and CSD.

Jul 30, 1993 - Vincent de Cordoba talks with Jane Jeans. She still has not received written approval from LeRC. Archie D'Arc calls Earl Marlborough at LeRC to prod LeRC personnel to see what has happened to the approval letter.

Aug 04, 1993 - Archie D'Arc calls Earl Marlborough for status on tracking down the approval letter. Earl Marlborough had not had time to track it down, but, after the phone call, he went to see Jim Stone, who was not in. Since Earl Marlborough is going out of own tomorrow, he asked Zack Buckshot to talk with Jim Stone tomorrow.

Aug 05, 1993 - Zack Buckshot talks with Jim Stone. Jim has sent the written approval to John Funn at Resistoglide. Zack Buckshot Faxes a copy of the letter to Archie D'Arc and Vincent de Cordoba. Archie D'Arc walks a copy of the Faxed letter over to Jane Jeans, who still has not seen a copy. Now that she has the letter, she will continue work on the 36Q's. CSD received a package today, dated July 27th, which includes the original letter of approval from Jim Stone to John Funn. Apparently, Resistoglide received the written approval a week ago, and it got delayed going through the internal distribution system.

Aug 09, 1993 - The 36Q for the VAX 4000/90 has not yet come out of Property Administration. John Toro will call Jane Jeans and someone from Property Administration to get it going. Now that the VAX has been approved and has an official number, the rest of the 36Q's covering the other components can go through the system. They should all go through quickly (!) with the exception of the 1553 cards. Since the 1553 cards are expensive, they will have to go through Property Administration screening just like the VAX did. What joy...

Aug 11, 1993 - John Toro leaves us a message. The EIEIO is back in Property Administration. It should go back to John Toro today or tomorrow, and then he can get the rest of the 36Q's going.

Aug 19, 1993 - Archie D'Arc calls John Toro to get the status of the 36Q's. Property Administration still has the package for the VAX 4000/90. The rest of the 36Q's cannot move until this comes back to John Toro. Archie D'Arc expresses to John Toro how important it is to get this through while LeRC is still our customer. We cannot afford to go through this process again with Popular Largeness as our new customer. John Toro calls back. He went to Property Administration to find out what is taking them so long. He was told that the package should be ready for him today, in an hour or two.

Aug 26, 1993 - We talk with John Toro for status. The 36Q for the VAX 4000/90 was at last given to Purchasing on August 23rd but has not yet been assigned a buyer. The 36Q for the 1553 cards is in Property Administration and will probably be there for a couple of weeks.

Aug 27, 1993 - Archie D'Arc calls John Dear, Purchasing Manager. John Dear says he assigned the VAX purchase to John Shoparound yesterday. John Shoparound is on vacation this week so he cannot start working on it until Monday at the earliest.

Aug 31, 1993 - John Shoparound calls Archie D'Arc to ask about the part numbers on the 36Q's for the 1553 transformers and connectors. Archie D'Arc asks about the 36Q for the VAX 4000/90. John Shoparound says that he has it and will take a look at it this morning.

Sep 01, 1993 - Jane Jeans calls Archie D'Arc to ask about the cost breakdown on two of the 36Q's regarding software licences. Jane Jeans said that these 36Q's have already made it through Property Administration, which "is common in cases where the first major component has been approved".

Sep 15, 1993 - CSD receives an IL from John Shoparound regarding the VAX 4000/90 purchase. DEC [the manufacturer] now feels that the VAX 4000/90 is at the end of its product life [unbelievable!!!] and does not want to sell this model to Resistoglide. They have proposed an alternative solution based on their new Alpha Workstation. John Shoparound has requested a technical evaluation of their proposal from us.

Sep 17, 1993 - Technical discussions with DEC personnel indicate that there is a fair bit of additional work to do before the technical evaluation of the Alpha Workstation can be completed. We must contact the manufacturers of the 1553 cards we plan to use to determine if their cards, and the software that drives those cards, are compatible with the new Alpha Workstation.

Sep 26, 1993 - Archie D'Arc calls Jane Jeans to get a status on the remaining 36Q's. Jane says that they have been approved by the on-site government regulation office and that she passed them back to Property Administration on September 22nd.

Sep 27, 1993 - Archie D'Arc calls John Toro to find out where the 36Q's might be. John investigates and finds out that they are still in Property Administration. John Toro later calls to say that Property Administration has delivered them back to him. John Toro will bring them over to Purchasing and request that John Shoparound be assigned as the buyer for these 36Q's since he is handling the rest of the 36Q's.

Sep 29, 1993 - Archie D'Arc talks with John Toro. John says that he was successful in getting John Shoparound to purchase the remaining equipment. John Shoparound will have the 36Q's by the end of the day.

Jan 20, 1994 - * * * *The Alpha computer actually arrives on the receiving dock.*** Elroy Yeager [of CSD] locates the 5 boxes on the dock but cannot remove them until a property tag has been placed on the computer.

Jan 24, 1994 - A 6.6 earthquake centered in Northridge causes major damage to the Resistoglide facility. The existing computers for simulation development and software testing sustain considerable water damage. Fortunately, the new Alpha sitting on the receiving dock was still packaged and did not get damaged.   Archie D'Arc and Elroy Yeager find Rob Lentil (the Director of Manufacturing) who approves the removal of the computer from the dock due to "unusual circumstances". After ten months of battling the procurement process and half an hour of looking for a safe way out of the damaged shipping and receiving building, the computer we needed for testing the control system and software for the Space Station's Electric Power System was finally delivered to our lab.

[No one would have ever believed it had it not been written down.]

Printed in the United States
5856

9 780741 401250